THE CENTURION

Also by Leonard Wibberiey

McGillicuddy McGotham
The Island of the Angels
A Feast of Freedom
A Mouse On the Moon
Mrs. Searwood's Secret Weapon
The Mouse That Roared
Take Me To Your President
Beware of the Mouse
Quest of Excalibur
Stranger At Killknock

THE CENTURION

Leonard Wibberley

William Morrow & Company, Inc.
New York 1966

Published simultaneously in Canada by
George J. McLeod Limited, Toronto.

Printed in the United States of America.

Library of Congress Catalog Card Number 66-24963

BOOK I

CHAPTER ONE

In the darkness of the predawn, the cold was intense and the centurion, sitting hunched on the side of his pallet bed, was glad of the bowl of hot wine, sweetened with wild honey, that his servant, Ruafocus, had brought him on awakening. The centurion held the bowl in his hands to warm them, and breathed in the fragrance of the wine, both to nourish his brain with the fumes and to warm it as well, as he had been told to do many years ago by a Greek physician. Now and again he shuddered, as much from the shock of awakening as from the cold in the small, mud-walled hut which constituted his quarters. He was getting old. As a young man he would not, however cold, have permitted himself such shudders for they were altogether unbecoming in a soldier.

"What time is it?" he asked Ruafocus, and the servant, who had achieved in age a tirelessness that was quite mechanical said, "The fourth hour," and went on blowing the brazier to make the charcoal glow more brightly. His hair was white and shoulder length and had the coarseness of a horsetail. His face was white too, despite a life spent out in all weathers, or perhaps it would be better to say that it was gray as the ashes of charcoal are gray. He had a long face, narrow and lined, with no fat on it. Under the tough skin were the remnants of tough muscles. His arms were sticks moved, as it were, by leather thongs or straps beneath the skin. Eying him in the glow of the brazier, the centurion reflected that it was hard to believe that this man had once been a warrior. Now in his old age he was reduced to the work of women—cooking and taking care of the centurion's personal needs.

"You were better dead," he said, speaking his thoughts.

"Of that no man can judge," said Ruafocus. "It is true," he added, "that one never hears complaints from the dead. But on the other hand I have received no word from my ancestors that their world is full of joy."

"It is better for a man to die young in battle than to live to an old age and blow on braziers," said the centurion.

"Why then," replied Ruafocus, "don't fight so hard in your next encounter. Expose your belly to the sword. Receive the steel with joy."

The centurion gave a slight grunt of a laugh. "Somehow," he said, "that is not my nature. But I will not spend my old age blowing on braziers."

"Roman," said Ruafocus, "you are not the master of your fate. You command a hundred men now. Ten years from now you will perhaps not command a child."

The centurion received this in silence because it was true. To the best of his belief he was fifty years of age. He had spent thirty-three years with the legions and served in eight campaigns. He could, whenever he wished, resign his commission in the army and return to Rome, or rather to Flavium, the little village in Liguria where he had been born. He would have a pension and there was a farm of three acres which belonged to him. Occasionally he remembered being on the farm, remembered being schooled and flogged by a schoolmaster who taught the children of several families; remembered snowfalls and mushrooms and the softness of the wind in the mountain pines. But he remembered them as if they had happened to someone else—someone who had died and whose place on earth had been taken by himself when he entered the army of what had been then the Republic of Rome.

He had a great deal of sympathy and indeed love for the lone boy on the farm in Liguria and thought of him at times as still being there, puzzled and lost. But he had no way of getting back to him and there would be nothing to say to him when they met because they would be strangers. He had been born again when he took service with Legion XX Valeria Victrix and went to Britain. He had served with five legions in all until he now was one of the sixty centurions of Legion X, Fretensis, whose headquarters were in Caesarea. The Tenth Legion, being on occupation duty in Judaea, was scattered throughout the country in various posts, each under the command of a centurion. All the centurions were Romans, but the legionnaries were for the most part Syrians and therefore auxiliaries and soldiers of the second class. The centurion, Longinus, believed privately that the occupation of Judaea would be more peaceful if the soldiers were all Romans, for the Syrians loathed the Jews and made as much trouble as they settled. But that was not possible. The empire was now too big to be policed by a purely Roman army and so foreign mercenaries had to be used.

Longinus was the senior centurion at Capernaum, which was a town of some size on the northwest corner of the Sea of Galilee in the Tetrarchy of Herod Antipas. It was a place of some economic importance, and it had also a strategic value for it was a fishing port on the Sea of Galilee and vessels crossing from the Greek city of Gergesa in Ituraea, which was in the Tetrarchy of Philip, put in there. These ships often carried passengers, sometimes fugitives, and it was the responsibility of the centurion at Capernaum to keep a watch on the traffic across the sea and find out where the passengers came from and where they were going. With such authority, Longinus could have added to his salary by accepting bribes. But he never took them, though he did not pretend anger when they were offered. Few had ever seen him angry; his anger was aroused only over some gross military offense among his men, and such offenses were rare. To the Jews, the fact that the centurion would not take bribes was a matter of some wonder, for they were well aware that at the bigger military post at Tiberias or Caesarea bribes were offered and received with impunity. They sought a reason for it.

"He is afraid of being discovered and reduced to the ranks in his old age," some said.

"The bribes are not big enough here at Capernaum," said others. "Move him to Tiberias, nearer to Herod, and he would soon start taking them. There are no poor Romans in Tiberias."

To the extent that it was possible for them to like a man who represented a foreign and occupying army, the Jews at Capernaum liked the centurion and would have been dismayed had another been sent to relieve him. He had, among other kindnesses, helped them rebuild their synagogue, setting his soldiers to work on a new road to the structure and strengthening the walls and putting in an outer court. Since this was work done by gentiles, the place had had to be thoroughly purified before use, but the centurion had not resented this though other Romans would have been outraged.

The fact was that he had served in so many lands among so many people of different customs that he had developed complete acceptance of any custom and took nothing as an insult either to himself or to Rome. In any case it was the policy of Rome to allow people their religion so long as Rome owned their land. Rebuilding the synagogue was in accordance with Rome's policy as administered by Pilate, the procurator in Caesarea.

As for himself the centurion had no religion. When he was a boy he had been surrounded by gods and by demons; gods of war, of love, of tillage, of rain, of flocks and of seasons. And demons and spites that attempted to interfere in all these matters. But all these things belonged to the boy who had been left on the little farm at Flavium. The void created by their absence was filled by the legion and the eagle of the legion. He performed the worship prescribed for soldiers under the regulations of the army as part of a soldier's duty. He made the necessary sacrifices decently and respectfully but never discussed his beliefs. There were the gods and there were men, and the arrangement suited him. It was possible that there was even one supreme god, or even one supreme single god as the Jews insisted. But this was not his business. His business was the welfare and the discipline of his century of men and the policing of the district that came under his control. It was on a matter of policing that he was up so early this morning.

It was a routine matter. Another prophet had appeared in the wilderness on the other side of the Jordan. That was where they always appeared. In fifteen years of occupation duty, the centurion had learned that there was a connection between wilderness and prophets. His name was John, which the centurion knew (for he could speak Aramaic) meant "Gift of God." John was haranguing the people about the coming of the liberator, which was the topic of all wilderness prophets. There was no difference between this one and a dozen others, except that this one said that the liberator was already born though even the Jews would not recognize him until his time had come.

It was this part that intrigued the centurion, for there was a hint of conspiracy here. Because conspiracy was something to which he was always alert he would find this Gift of God living in the wilderness and listen to him and see whether he was dangerous or merely slightly mad.

Ruafocus had now prepared the centurion's breakfast, a pancake in which was rolled up some boiled and shredded goat's meat seasoned with onions. The centurion was indifferent to food and ate as a matter of necessity, which annoyed Ruafocus.

"The onions are Syrian," he said. "King's onions." That because they were purple. "You chew them like hay."

"I was thinking of prophets," said the centurion.

"You are becoming a Jew," said Ruafocus, who was himself a Celt and still had the blue tattoo marks of his tribe, which was that of the Deer, on his thin arm and torso. "This country is thicker with prophets than a sheep with burrs. They cannot live without them."

"I wonder why that should be," said the centurion.

"They have no contentment," said Ruafocus. "Everything is going to happen tomorrow. They spit on today. If they have a god he will destroy them for that."

"Why?" asked the centurion.

"Because today is the gift the gods make to men. To

throw it aside and look for some further gift which is called tomorrow is insulting to the gods. If you have received a present from the gods, it is bad manners to belittle it because you believe there will be a better one coming. When you are as old as I am you will know what a great gift each day is."

"What gods have you?" asked the centurion, though he knew the answer, having served in Britain.

"Our gods are dead," said the Celt. "Your gods were more powerful than ours. They have killed ours."

"So why not worship mine?"

"Yours will be killed too. There is a new god coming."

"How do you know that?"

Ruafocus made no reply but squatted before the brazier staring at the glowing charcoal. His statement intrigued the centurion, and although this talk of gods was foreign to him, he was curious and wondered whether his servant had heard among the Jews something that he should know.

"How do you know that?" he repeated.

"I cannot say," said Ruafocus. "It is a thing that has come to me."

"You have heard something?"

Ruafocus was still staring at the glowing charcoal. Without taking his eyes off the coals he said, "Last night I heard the wind in the forests of my own land. I have not heard it for thirty years. It was cool on my skin and I could smell the sap of the deep ferns very clean and sweet." He turned and looked at the centurion anxiously. "You did not feel the wind and smell the growth? The wind was soft."

"You dreamed," said the centurion. "You heard the wind off the sea."

Ruafocus shook his head. "There is no wind blows in the world like the wind in my own forests," he said. "I heard it and I felt it on my skin. It is a sign."

"If it's a sign, what is it a sign of?" asked the centurion.

"It is a sign that everything will be born again and we are all to be made as we were when we were young."

The centurion got heavily off the pallet and went to a stand on which was a bowl of water. He put his hands into the water and dashed some of it over his face. With the water dripping off him he turned to his servant.

"You dream of your forests and I remember Flavium," he said. "We are both dead men. Dead long ago. We have a comradeship in that, you and I. What we have left is ourselves and a little time."

He dried his face. "Those and the legion," he concluded.

CHAPTER TWO

The journey to the place where the new prophet was speaking to the people took four days. It lay not really in the wilderness beyond the Jordan but on the banks of the river in the lowlands where it poured through a lush valley into the Salt Sea. Another officer, a centurion of lower rank, could have been sent on the mission, of course. But Longinus wished to inspect the military posts on the road, over which he had authority, and gather at first hand the reports of the centurions in charge; for he would himself soon have to journey to Caesarea and report to the tribune, Gaius Servius, a young man who was newly out from Rome in the court of Pilate and to whom he was directly responsible.

The line of command in the legion in Judaea was divided for the legion performed a twofold task. On the one hand it was a civil and policing agency, its members often occupied in public works such as road improvement or the building of aqueducts. As a policing agency, related to a civil authority, it was responsible, in his area, to the Tetrarch Herod Antipas, the puppet king approved by Rome, whose territory included Galilee to the west of the Jordan and the Sea of the same name, and Peraea, which lay east of the Jordan below the Sea of Galilee and extended halfway down the Salt Sea on its eastern side.

Galilee was Jewish, but Peraea was Greek. Here people were freer of the strait-laced government of the priests and took their pleasures in an atmosphere without censure. There were noble public baths in such cities as Bethabara, Pella, Gerasa and, to the south, Philadelphia and Machaerus; and there were also forums for gladiatorial combats and racing, and gymnasiums, abhorred by the Jews for reasons neither the Greeks nor Romans could understand since they saw nothing base in exercises performed naked.

The cities of Peraea were pleasant—laid out with room and with fine temples and public buildings, whereas the Jewish cities, even Jerusalem, were crowded together, house crowding next to house as if all were in fear of the wild mountains around. The northern portion of Peraea was called Decapolis, which meant "ten cities." The centurion didn't know to what ten cities the name referred, but Herod Antipas, though himself technically a Jew, was a lover of the Greeks and favored Peraea and spent much of the public funds on that portion of his territory. In Peraea there were statues to the gods and shrines and decorations on the buildings—all things prohibited in Jewish Galilee, so that the Romans had a saying that happiness lay beyond the Jordan.

But outside of these pleasure-loving cities, there were vast areas of wilderness—stark mountainous deserts stripped for the greater part of the year of any growth. The mountains were eroded down to the rocks which formed their skeletons, all topsoil having been stripped away by wind and rain. These mountainous places were impossible territories for military operations and were thus the habitat of brigands. And prophets.

As a military body the legion was responsible to Pontius Pilate, the procurator of Judaea. This land encompassed the territories between the Jordan and the Great Sea to the west, including then Judaea itself and also Samaria, which lay between Judaea and Galilee to the north.

Pilate had been appointed by the Emperor Tiberius. The Emperor was supreme commander of the army and since Pilate was his personal representative in Judaea it followed also that he commanded the army there. The situation was a delicate one though it pleased Pilate hugely. He loved to intrigue from a position of power and he had that position of power—the ear of the emperor and the real command of the legions.

The two tetrarchs, Herod Antipas and his brother, Herod Philip, the king of Ituraea, were puppets. Pilate teased them by pretending to defer to their positions. He honored them in their territories and honored them publicly. But, using the legions, he obtained detailed intelligence from their areas which, reported to Rome, did them no credit. The mission of the senior centurion, Longinus, would add to that intelligence, but Longinus had to be careful. In reporting to Pilate through the tribune, he must be sure not to slight Herod Antipas. He would turn over to Herod only what he judged concerned him. The full report would go to Caesarea.

The centurion took with him on his mission Ruafocus and three other men, among them an old comrade, Balba, who, like himself and unlike the others, was a Roman. Balba was a short powerful man with a very red face; he was fond of wine for which he had an immoderate capacity. Drunkenness on duty was an offense for which a soldier could be scourged, but Balba was never drunk to incapacity though Longinus was of the opinion that he was never really sober either. His eyesight was impaired, but he did his work competently, and spoke little, though he was by no means surly. Balba maintained that his eyes had been damaged during service on the Rhine when in a small skirmish his face had been smashed in by the shield of one of the enemy. There was room, in the damage to his face, for believing this story. The left cheekbone and the nose were crushed, so that Balba snuffled heavily in breathing. But Longinus held that it was wine as much as the shield of a German warrior that had damaged Balba's eyes. They were pale blue, red-rimmed and watery. He had, of course, no front teeth and, far from handsome, was called "The Beauty" among the men.

Women, of the sort with which he could have any acquaintance, liked him however—Longinus had noted that women of all races, except very young ones, were careless of the looks of men and were often attracted to very ugly men by some quality which he had never been able to identify.

Longinus' small patrol was mounted on horses, even Ruafocus, who, as servant to the centurion, should either have walked or, speed beyond a foot pace being necessary, been mounted on an ass. But Ruafocus would ride nothing but a horse. From the day he entered the centurion's service he had set his own terms and they had been honored.

An ass was below his dignity, as was a mule. Indeed he did not like to ride a mare, though he would consent to do so. But given his choice of a mount, he would take a stallion or a gelding. He had a talent for handling horses yet rode in a curious manner without saddle or bridle or even a saddle blanket. He rode bareback and guided his horse with a stick, touching the neck on one side or the other to point it in a particular direction in the manner of camel riders. In this style, that of his people, he had as a youth ridden ten hours without fatigue, though, older now, he was sometimes tired at the end of a day.

On his journey Longinus found, at each post he passed, little that was not normal though there was, as he went south, more disturbance about the prophet he was seeking. He expected to hear of miracles since that was usual with prophets and he did not doubt that some of them were capable of performing such wonders, for they were known in all lands and from all times. But this prophet, it seemed, had performed no miracles, so it was strange that he should command such respect and cause such excitement.

It was reported at the post at Bethabara that the prophet had gone through there a week previously, headed south along the Jordan. He had been accompanied by two or three men who were civil enough, but the prophet himself looked mad, dressed in goatskins which he had wrapped around him without trying to make a proper garment of them.

"You questioned him?" asked Longinus of the centurion in command of the post at Bethabara.

"Yes. I asked him whether he was not John the son of Zachary and Elizabeth who are from some settlement in the north. I think it is Bethany. That is the information that was given to me."

"What did he say?"

"He said he was a voice in the wilderness. I asked him what he meant by that. He said that he was a voice in the wilderness as the wind is a voice in the wilderness. He said that as the wind does not speak for itself but for its master which causes it to blow, so also he spoke for his master."

"And who did he say was his master?"

"To that he would give me no answer. He said he is preparing a road for his master to travel on." The centurion grinned. "Him and the two others with him, I suppose. Won't be much of a road."

"And your opinion?" asked Longinus.

"A cracked jug," said the other. "It holds nothing and, struck, gives out no round sound."

But Ruafocus, impressed by the reference to the wind because of his dream, grew excited and said, "The wind is the key to it all. This man is a true seer."

The other centurion knew the liberties that the servant of Longinus took in interrupting a conversation between two Roman officers, and dared not rebuke him directly in the presence of Longinus himself. But he resented this intrusion and said to Ruafocus, "You sound like a cracked jug yourself."

"Bah," said Ruafocus. "You Romans are all blind. You resemble ants. You are all organization but you have to bump into things to find out that they are there."

"If you are not careful a Roman fist will bump into your old skull," said the centurion, losing his temper.

"It is a comfort to me in my old age," said Ruafocus softly, "to know that I have killed in my youth more Romans than you command."

The other who had a quick temper was now angry enough to strike the man but Longinus quieted him. "Leave him," he said. "He has the temper of his people. You are young and did not serve in Britain. What he says is true. In his day he was as good a man as you and I ever were."

"I do not like this talk of killing Romans," said the other. "He should keep his mouth shut."

"His people killed many of us," said Longinus. "My father was but one of them. They would have killed me too, but for him."

That concluded the interview and left Longinus with little more knowledge of the prophet except that his parents had been named Elizabeth and Zachary and were of the tribe of David. This information had been volunteered to the centurion of Bethabara by one of the two men who were with the prophet. He had added that both were in their old age when the son was born and it was for this reason that he had been named not Zachary but John—the Gift of God.

"His birth was foretold by an angel," one of the followers of the prophet had said. "And his father was a priest and had been elected to make the offering to The Holy Place when the angel appeared to him. He was struck dumb and remained dumb until the son was born."

This was not an unusual pattern for a prophet, Longinus reflected as he continued on his way. The birth was always unusual, there was an angel somewhere in the background and the prophet took to the wilderness.

"It is surprising," he said reflectively to Ruafocus, "that they never have a prophet from Jerusalem, which is their holy city." He thought about this for some time and then answered himself, "Revolts never start in cities," he said. "They always start in the countryside. In the cities there is a great deal to do and much entertainment. In the country there is no diversion and people brood over their grievances. That is the reason."

"In the country the wind blows freely," said Ruafocus.

Farther along the road when, on the following day, they had crossed the bridge over the Jordan to gain the eastern bank of the river, they neared an area of swampland. The road forked here. The better road led eastward to round the swamps, going to the fringe of foothills through which, in the rainy season, a score of rivulets dashed down from the hills to feed the Jordan flood. The other fork of the road, useless during the rainy season, led through the swamp area. Even in the dry season it was avoided by wheeled traffic and horse litters, for there were many places where the soft ground made going impossible. But the centurion decided to take this lower road which led through high growths of bulrushes and papyrus and saw grass.

This was known as The Place of the Birds, for it was the haunt of herons and storks and wild ducks, but it might also have been known as the place of the snakes for there were many of them about—asps and vipers and others which were bigger but said to be nonpoisonous. The snakes hunted the small animal life of the swamplands and supplemented their diet with eggs and fledglings. There was a brooding watchfulness about the lush greenery, and as the party passed through, their nerves were strained by the sudden whirring of bird wings as a flock of duck or heron rose out of the growth on either side.

"A good place for an ambush," said Balba. "Why do we go this way, Centurion?"

"Because we have never been this way before," replied the other. "I have thought about it but never done so. Now we have an opportunity."

"There will be no taverns," said Balba.

"Then suck on your memories," said the centurion. "There is enough wine in them to keep you from thirst."

"Memories don't slake the thirst," said Balba. "They but add to it."

They made camp in a slightly raised area where the dark ground was a little firmer. The area, perhaps from some change of the chemistry of the soil, was clear of the big reeds and bulrushes, though there were some thickets of thorns growing on it. These were cleared and a ditch dug around the area and the thorns used as a barricade around the camp. The senior centurion was meticulus about such preparation. It was a regulation of the army that no military unit, however small, should camp without a trench around its encampment and a barricade inside the trench. Others paid but superficial service to this regulation, but Longinus regarded all regulations of the army as sacred and saw that the work was thoroughly done, fortifying the encampment of his four men with the same care with which he would have fortified the encampment of a full century or a cohort.

He worked at the business himself but sent Ruafocus off to get what game he could in the swamp, for he was skilled both in snaring birds and bringing them down with a slingshot. Because of the heights of the reeds around, which towered over his head, Ruafocus left his sling behind; there would not be room to give him free movement of his arm. He disappeared into the thickets of reeds, all tawny at the bottom but lush with green and gold at the tops, hissing a little as he went. He hissed as a precaution against snakes, to warn them of his coming, for he knew that they would not strike at him unless taken by surprise.

His hearing, despite his years, was acute, and he could hear to the sides and in front of him little rustles and scurryings which told of reptiles and mammals moving aside to let him by. He made his way down toward the river and when he was close to the bank and could hear the thunder and gurgle of the water, which at this point moved over a rough bed, started to tie the tops of the reeds together so as to form an entanglement among them. He made this entanglement in the form of a semi-circle, stretching from north to south close to the river, and then cut a section of dry reed which he split down the middle several times. This done, he moved back away from his bird trap towards the roadway and then stopped cautiously, for in the humid air of the swamp he had caught a wisp of sweetish scent.

He waited immobile until an eddy of the air brought the scent to him again, and then he moved off in the direction from which the eddy had come. He found a place where the reeds had been bruised and some of them trampled down. It was not more than ten yards from the road but on the river side. The sweetish scent was stronger here. He pushed aside the thicket ahead of him and found the source of the scent: a man lying on the ground, his throat cut and his face splotched green and gray with advancing decay.

Ruafocus studied the man for a while, noted the richness of his clothing and the fact that the throat had been cut so savagely as nearly to cut off the head. He did not approach the corpse but stood ten feet or more from it, taking in all the details and looking at the bulrushes around, and then returned to hunt birds.

He went to a place which would put him above the arc of netting he had tied in the reeds and outside of it. Then he shouted and started to wave the split cane vigorously. This produced a brisk clacking sound, and there was a flurry and whirring of wings around him as frightened birds rose and flew down to the safety of the river. Some flew straight into the tanglement of reed which he had made, and by this method he secured four ducks and a heron, all of which had broken their necks flying into the reeds. These he paunched on the spot and took back to the camp with him. It was only when he was roasting the fowl that he reported to the centurion that there was a dead man lying down the road a quarter of a mile south of them.

"Why did you not tell me before?" demanded the centurion.

"Why hurry?" asked Ruafocus. "He has been dead several days by the look of him. He can wait until tomorrow."

"What kind of man is he?" asked centurion.

"A stinking man," said Ruafocus. "Rich, to judge by his clothes. There should be others about. Such a man would not journey through a place like this without a bodyguard."

"Perhaps his bodyguard killed him," said the centurion.

The sun had already dipped behind the hills of Samaria to the west and though the sky was bright, a deepening shadow lay over the valley of the Jordan and the swamp. The eastern hills which could just be seen over the swamp growth were tinged with the light of sunset and seemed to be afire, glowing like coals against the sky.

"We will find him tomorrow," said the centurion. "But you should have told me immediately."

"What do you prefer for your supper?" asked Ruafocus. "A stinking corpse or fresh game? An old campaigner like you should have no difficulty making a decision. Will you have duck or heron? There is more meat on the heron, but the flesh is muddy."

The centurion took duck, which pleased Ruafocus, for he preferred the heron himself. When they had finished eating, Ruafocus took the feathers, bones, and scraps of the birds and burned them carefully in the fire, lest the gods of these creatures know they had been destroyed and so be angry with him.

CHAPTER THREE

At first the centurion thought that the murdered man had been the victim of robbers for several bands were active in the countryside particularly where the road, leading from the north to south, the principal highway, passed through desert or swamp areas. The names of the leaders of these bands were known—Andreas ben Joseph, Dismas, Barabbas and so on. It was because of their presence as well as to maintain the road and keep an eye on the traveling population, that little companies of the legions were stationed along the highway. But there were some aspects in this instance that disturbed the centurion and suggested that this was not a case merely of robbery—and in fact that robbery was not the principal motive behind the murder.

First among these was the fact that the man had been killed. Among the Jews, even among their outlaws, the prohibition against killing under the law given by their leader Moses was of the strongest. A rabbi, explaining these laws to the centurion, had once pointed out that the first two referred to the worship of God, the next to the relationship between man and his family, and the fourth

—the first to deal with a man and his neighbors—was the commandment, "Thou shalt not kill."

"You will understand," said the rabbi gently but with a certain superiority, "that we hold the lives of all men as precious, to be taken only by God."

It was certainly true that murder among the Jews was a rarity, and so the centurion was of the opinion that the murdered man had been killed by non-Jews. Yet robbery on close investigation did not seem to be the motive. The victim had not been stripped of his clothes, which were precious possessions. He still had with him a leather wallet hidden among his robes containing a considerable sum of money in coin. His dress identified him as one of the Levites of the Temple in Jerusalem, and this added to the puzzle because such people were treated with marked deference even by brigands.

The centurion concluded that the murder was one of revenge by a Gentile, perhaps a Syrian or a Samaritan. Between Jew and Samaritan there was such animosity that no Jew would even mention the word "Samaritan" or speak to a Samaritan or travel through Samaria. He would cross the Jordan rather than do so.

Longinus asked Ruafocus his opinion of the killing and the servant said, "It was done with hate. The head is nearly cut off."

"A Samaritan or a Syrian," said the centurion. He told them to wrap the body in its outer garment or cloak and tie it on one of the horses. But the horse shied and kicked at carrying such a load, and only Ruafocus was able to calm it. This he did by taking some of the mud of the swamp and smearing it on the nostrils of the beast. The centurion had never seen this done before and asked the reason.

"So he cannot smell the death he carries," said

Ruafocus. "The mud smells of life to him and he will be less anxious. It is strange that you Romans should rule the world, yet not know these things."

"We rule those who do know them," said the centurion. "That is sufficient."

"You order everything but rule nothing," said Ruafocus.

"Take my stirrup and let us be on our way," said the centurion, for the dead man had been put on the servant's horse. In the heat of the swamp Ruafocus was soon sweating heavily and breathing hard from the exertion of keeping up with the horse even with the aid of the stirrup. The centurion glanced down at him from time to time and debated whether to let him ride behind. But in the soft ground the double weight would be hard on the horse. He then considered having Balba or one of the soldiers dismount so that Ruafocus could ride. But such a procedure went against his military conscience since Ruafocus was his personal property whereas the horses were the property of Rome and so should be ridden by those in the direct service of Rome.

After a while he reined in, dismounted, and told Ruafocus to get into the saddle.

"You are not entirely Roman," said Ruafocus when he had done so. "There is some heart in you but you fight it hard. Yet I do not think you will succeed in killing it." He became chatty now, which annoyed the centurion who wanted to save his breath for walking.

"When you find the prophet, what questions will you put to him?" the servant demanded.

To this the centurion made no reply.

"I will tell you what you will ask him," said Ruafocus. "First you will ask his name and he will tell you that.

Then his tribe and his place of birth, and he will tell you these things too. Then you will ask him what he preaches. He will answer you and you will not understand the answer but I will understand it and explain it to you."

"How is it you will understand and I will not?" asked the centurion, irritated.

"Because of our different positions," said Ruafocus. "You are a master and so can only look down. There is nothing around you to look at and nothing above you to look at and to inquire about. You can only look downward and with a mind already fixed so that it is not open to new ideas. But I am a servant and must look around me and upwards and always with my mind open, for a servant can have no fixed opinion but must be ready at all times to receive a new view.

"It is the hardest position in the world to be a master for then everything must be made to follow a pattern and so all becomes of one color and of one voice. But the life of a servant is full of variety, of tones and colors and voices and there is no dullness. I assure you that although authority may lie with masters, yet wisdom lies with servants and if a master wishes to be wise, he should consult his servants in all important matters."

This idea was so ridiculous that the centurion laughed. "The perfect world then would be run by a slave," he said.

"Not a slave," said Ruafocus, "but a man of . . ." Then he stopped for he could not find the word he needed, though what he meant was quite clear in his own mind. "There is no word for it," he said, "but the kind of man I have in mind would be one who cared for all men."

"More nonsense," said the centurion. "And I will prove it to you." He had taken a course in rhetoric when he was a boy and prided himself that he had done well at it. "Let us suppose that this man of yours cared for the Samaritans. If he really cared for them he must hate the Jews. Again if he cared for the Jews he must hate the Samaritans. How then could a man care for all men?" He was pleased with the little exposition, which silenced Ruafocus for a while.

"He would care for something that is in all men, whether they are Jews or Samaritans," he replied at length. "He would show every man that he had this thing and must respect it in others."

Balba was riding behind them and out of boredom joined the conversation. "He will give them all wine," he said. "Wine makes people feel good together."

"It will have to be a new kind of wine," said the centurion, "for after a little wine most men quarrel."

"You are an ignorant people," said Ruafocus. "The Egyptians and the Greeks do your thinking for you, for you are afraid of thought. If in talking together you come close to a truth, just to the very hem of it, then you make a joke of it. You are afraid of truth. I believe that is what you Romans are afraid of—truth."

The centurion wanted to make a reply to this—to point out that truth was what men made it. But he doubted that Ruafocus would understand that, and anyway Balba quoted an old saying that truth lay in wine so that the grape was the fruit of knowledge even though the Jews said it was the apple, which only grew in Syria anyway and not in their land.

"The wine of apples will make you sick," he said. "Pomona is a vicious wench in my view, but Bacchus loves his worshipers and never did them real harm."

It was while they were talking like this that they

emerged gradually from the swampland and the reeds and came to a broken, rocky area of high land well above the river's flood mark. The place was very wild and dotted here and there with thorn bushes with thin, oily leaves and an occasional rag of pink blossom. The road was nothing more than a path winding over this area, up first to the brow of a hill and then down to a broad boulder-strewn valley beyond.

The climate changed immediately they had reached this desert highland. The close dampness of the swamp, with its heavy silence broken only by bird flight and the rustle of their horses through the growth, was replaced by a crisp, clean wind coming off the mountains to the east. This wind seemed to cleanse the very air so that it was possible to see a great distance with no blurring even of the edges of the farthest objects. Immediately they all felt invigorated and more cheerful, and Ruafocus noted that the flies no longer buzzed around the body of the Levite on the horse to the rear of them. The centurion, who had remounted his horse, reined in, looking over the valley, which was like an enormous natural amphitheater. Far away to the west he could see, a living glitter among the rocks, the sparkle of the Jordan. The road ran down toward it but there was no habitation in sight. A little distance to the east of the road, that is, on the side of it away from the river, he saw a movement and, shielding his eyes with his hand against the glare of sky and desert, made out a solitary figure climbing up the hill or side of the amphitheater away from the road. At that distance the figure was no bigger than the joint of one of his fingers; but he knew immediately, without knowing how, that this was the prophet whom he was seeking. He watched him climb up the hill, going quite fast despite the roughness of the ground.

"Take the men along the road to the first post," he said to Balba. "You will find it four miles from here over the brow of the hill. I will meet you there. I will go on alone."

"Am I to come with you?" asked Ruafocus.

"No," said the centurion. "With this man I will speak privately."

CHAPTER FOUR

"You are the centurion at Capernaum," said the prophet when they met. "A man marked by God to be born again, so that you may bear witness to him, as I also bear witness to him. Though you are dead now, yet you will live again."

The centurion was not greatly surprised by these words, for he was well acquainted with the habit of these prophets of the Jews of talking in astounding terms and making individual prophecies which sent men of less knowledge into ecstasy or despair. It did not even greatly surprise him that the prophet John should have identified him as the centurion at Capernaum, for he well knew that the Jews kept track of his movements and thus news of where he was going often preceded his arrival.

"In the course of one life a man lives many lives," said the centurion. "The seven ages of man are well known and each constitutes a separate life for man into which he is born, leaving a corpse of himself behind." He was thinking of his boyhood and the farm at Flavium.

The prophet smiled at him with warm pleasure. He was a handsome man, at least twenty years younger than the centurion, big for a Jew, with dark hair and a dark beard.

The centurion speculated that he did not come from any of the tribes of Galilee, where the people tended to fairness and many had hazel rather than brown eyes. The eyes of this man were blue, which was a surprise though not entirely unknown.

"I see you are a man who has taken thought and is not given to the superstitions of the Gentiles," he said. "Your body wears harness but not your mind. Does not the harness of the body weigh down your spirit?"

"I do my duty to my master, though the pay is small," said the centurion. "Some say we should be paid more."

The prophet laughed. "You cannot trap me," he said. "I do not preach sedition among the soldiers of Rome. Many have come to me on this question—many of Ceasar's soldiers as well as those of Herod—and I have told them to be content with their pay. My master is not concerned with such matters."

"And who is your master?" asked the centurion.

"One the latchet of whose sandal I am not worthy to loose." The phrase indicated a position lower even than that of a slave, for it was the duty of a slave, when his master returned to his house, to remove his sandals and bathe his feet.

"Ceasar?" asked the centurion, mockingly.

"One the latchet of whose sandal Caesar is not worthy to loose," said the prophet.

"Put a guard on your tongue," said the centurion. "If I were to repeat what you say, that phrase could cost you your head."

The prophet gave him a look containing neither fear nor anger. "Do you seek the truth, Roman?" he asked. "Or do you come to question me to snare me? The truth will live forever and a lie will forever corrupt. What do you want, Roman? The truth or only such pieces of the truth as can be turned into lies so that I may be put into the dungeon of Herod as a threat to his authority? And if this is done, do you think that the truth will be imprisoned in the dungeon with me, never more to be abroad in the world?"

"Tell me for whom you speak and for what purpose," said the centurion.

"I am come to prepare the coming of another," said the prophet. "I am one who straightens the road for the king, and sees that all are ready to receive him. I move aside the boulders and fill in the pits and point out the places of foulness so that they may be cleansed beyond the whiteness of snow for his coming."

"What king?" the centurion persisted.

"He who shall lead the way through death to eternal life."

The centurion had heard that definition before and thought he knew now of whom the prophet spoke. "Mithras?" he asked, for Mithras was the son of one of the gods who had taken human form, freed the people of their wrongs, been put to death and risen from the dead. His worship was semisecret but existed among some of the men of the legions, where it was tolerated so long as the worshipers made the official sacrifices to the Roman gods. There was a growing belief that Mithras would reappear soon in human form.

For answer the prophet pointed to a gleaming rock of limestone which cast a dark shadow on the ground a few feet away. "As that shadow is to that rock, so is Mithras to him of whom I speak," said the prophet. "One is but the evidence of the substance while the other is the substance itself—the truth and the word and the way, whose coming has been echoed through all time as footsteps are heard approaching in a dark valley at night though no one is seen."

"You speak then of your Messiah," said the centurion.

"Him whom they call the Messiah and of whom the prophets spoke," said John.

The centurion had, at the start of the interview, dismounted from his horse and was squatting on his haunches beside the prophet. He sat with his back to the rocks of a cliff which was seemingly the prophet's habitation. There was no cave here but only an overhanging ledge which would keep off the rain but provide little shelter against the wind. The centurion squinted his eyes against the sun and stared across the glittering valley whose stones, now that evening was approaching, glowed red on the tops though the shadows were deep blue and even purple. He thought about the prophet and the land that had produced him.

The prophet was plainly just one of those harmless and deranged figures that the Jews, more than any other people of whom he had knowledge, produced. Too much thinking, too much reading of their scrolls, too much loneliness and privation and yearning unbalanced them. Their religion, depriving them of all natural pleasures, of women and wine in abundance, of games and gambling and extravagances, aggravated their condition. They were a people driven mad by their god and yet they clung to this god of theirs and died by the hundreds for him. And what had he given them? Harsh living, a land that was fruitful indeed in the river valley but elsewhere utterly barren; a place for goats and the skinniest of sheep. And this they called their Promised Land.

It was ludicrous how they loved it, how sacred they held it. There were Jews in all parts of the Empire, in Rome itself and throughout Italy and even in Gaul and in Syria and Greece and Pontos. They knew the beauty of the earth in other places, the lush valleys, the flowering acres of Scythia, the palms and the fruits and herds of fat cattle. And still they prized this miserable minor Egypt, returned faithfully to it, believed it to have been given to them for all time by their god and believed also that their god would some day send them a deliverer who would secure this land for them forever.

He shook his head and said aloud, "Preserve me from such a god, who hates those who worship him."

"You do not know him," said the prophet. "God does not exist for the pleasure of man. Nor does man live for his own pleasure, but to serve God by good works."

The centurion shrugged. The formula was so old that it had lost all color and meaning for him. Indeed it irritated him as being a subterfuge, pretending to knowledge but containing nothing. He looked at the prophet, strong, young, and because he was such a well-made man he felt sorry for him because of the inevitable end that he knew from past experience lay ahead of him.

"You would do well not to talk about this Messiah," he said. "It will lead to your death on a charge of sedition. There is a big world about for you to enjoy. You are a young man. Forget the Messiah and enjoy the world."

"I am the servant of God," said the prophet. "Does the servant turn from his master to his own enjoyment?"

"Then think of others," said the centurion. "Think of your own people living in little villages and isolated farms, making of their lives what they can. Think of men crucified and children butchered and farms of little more than an acre, representing a hundred years' toil, turned back into desert because you preach the coming of this Messiah. Leave them in peace."

"The people are the servants of God as am I. Would you, called to duty as a soldier, refuse because to obey would bring suffering on others?"

"Rome exists," said the centurion. "There are a thousand gods—or none. It is a matter of belief." He was thirsty and thought of asking the prophet for a drink but then decided that the man himself probably drew his water from the river and would have but a small store.

The prophet perceived that he was thirsty for he took a bowl of clay, and held it against the face of the rock that sheltered them. The rock was of a gray color, but turned darker immediately above the bowl and a trickle of water exuded from it, filling the bowl which the prophet gave to the centurion. Instead of drinking the water the centurion arose, drew his sword, and struck the rock several blows, to break through the outer casing to the reservoir of water which he believed must lie behind. He used his sword with the force of a blacksmith using a hammer. But though he made a deep notch in the rock at the point where the prophet had filled the bowl, the stone was dry and no water issued from it.

The prophet was laughing gently. "You are puzzled?" he asked, plainly enjoying himself.

"No," said the centurion. "It is a trick. There is water in a catchment behind the face of the rock."

"Then why does it come at my wish but not at the summons of your sword?" asked the prophet. "What do you think?"

"You know the trick," said the other.

"I had expected better of you," said the prophet in

gentle reproof. "Truly at present you are a dead man and seek answers from dead things. But when you are born again and come to life you will seek answers from living things and what is now hidden from you will be plain before your eyes."

"How may I be born again?" asked the centurion.

"Seek the truth," said the prophet. "The truth will be denied to none who earnestly seek it. And may the peace of God go with you."

"Where shall I seek the truth?" persisted the centurion.

"Seek and you will find the way," said the prophet. "Be brave, soldier. It will be a way of sorrows."

CHAPTER FIVE

Gaius Servius was but one of the six tribunes of the Tenth Legion whose headquarters were at Jerusalem, though, as noted, the legion itself was scattered in various posts throughout Judaea. On arrival from Rome he should have proceeded to Jerusalem with his staff, but, pleading the weather, at that time very hot, and the fatigue of his journey, he had contrived to remain at Caesarea where things went more in the Roman way so that there were plenty of amusements for him, banquets, gladiatorial combats, races of both men and horses, and a sophistication which he was sure Jerusalem would lack. He had been told it lacked all these things.

Also Pontius Pilate, the procurator, was quartered at the time in a splendid Grecian palace at Caesarea he had constructed or, rather, remodeled himself. The young tribune felt his ambitions would be better served if he stayed close to Pilate—watching Pilate and attending at his court rather than serving as an officer swallowed in the organization of a legion which, being on garrison duty, offered little prospect of enrichment from booty.

His appointment was a political one, so he took up his quarters in a villa close to Pilate's palace with an excellent view of the harbor and the ocean beyond. He complained that this villa was lacking in appointments and grace when compared with his own on a hill to the north of Rome. Nothing suited him. All things filled him with a slight disgust, bringing a sigh from his ruby lips and a little flutter of a white, plump hand which was at once a protest and an acceptance. Gaius Servius was, or pretended to be, an Epicurean, a lover of only the best, a connoisseur equally of virtue and of vice which for him were amusing concepts of the Stoics, quite without significance. Since he was new from Rome, and knew the latest gossip of Roman society—anecdotes about emperor and senators, all deliciously told—he was for a while the center of the society of Caesarea and even the manner in which he wore his toga was copied by those who loved the Roman way.

That Gaius Servius had influence, Pilate knew, for otherwise he would not have secured from the Senate his appointment as tribune. Pilate's own correspondent in Rome had written him secretly about his new officer, hinting that his influence came through Piso, who was rumored to have caused the death of Germanicus by poison; a death not displeasing, it was said, to the Emperor Tiberius.

"Entertain him well, and watch him as well as you entertain him," one correspondent wrote. "Do not fail to smile at his sallies and humor him but guard your laughter in any witticisms he may make about the emperor for these, seeming imprudent, are often made with a purpose."

From this Pilate gathered that the new tribune, far from being a counselor for him in the affairs of the legion, was an agent of others in Rome who coveted the position of procurator of Judaea for themselves. He was quite content to allow the tribune to dally at Caesarea where he could keep a watch on his activities. He entertained him and encouraged him to neglect his military duties while being scrupulous that, in matters of military precedent, the position of the tribune was always honored.

It was to this man then that Longinus, the senior centurion at Capernaum, came to submit his report on the state of the extensive district under his control. He had sent a written report, dictated to a secretary, to the tribune three weeks ahead of his own arrival, but when he reached Caesarea he was kept waiting a further week in the soldier's quarters of the praetorium before the tribune summoned him for questioning.

He found the tribune not in an audience chamber but seated on the terrace of his villa, which had been turned into a marketplace; there was merchandise of many kinds, though all of the highest quality, lying around with the slaves ready to show whatever was required. The centurion recognized, standing behind the tribune's chair, Joseph of Antioch, who, although a Syrian, was dressed in the Greek fashion. It said something for the wealth and importance of the tribune that Joseph of Antioch should be present himself, for he sold personally only to the most influential of clients, and his own importance was such that the centurion had many times, at Pilate's orders, sent a special escort to guard a consignment of Joseph's goods passing through the wilder parts of his district.

This man in the past had sent the centurion one or two gifts which the centurion had returned. He never passed through Capernaum without speaking to the centurion and on a friendly basis. But now, as the centurion entered and made his way through all the glitter of this impromptu market on the terrace—bolts of lovely silks, stacks of beautiful rugs and carpets so soft as to feel like cool moss to the touch, chests, statues of marble, wood and ivory—through all these treasures then, Joseph gave him a look which, while it held recognition, held no warmth.

"Ah, Longinus," said the tribune, "you have come in time to rescue me. This kook is fleecing me, a poor Roman newly out from our little capital on the Tiber." The word "kook" shocked the centurion. It was often used by the Romans among themselves in talk about Jews, Syrians and other foreigners, but only the coarsest of them used it in the presence of the foreigners themselves who resented it acutely. Yet Gaius the tribune used it in a light way, as if there was so much understanding between him and Joseph of Antioch that the latter would appreciate the use of the word as a token of this intimacy. Indeed Joseph was smiling, but the smile was forced and the centurion could see that the merchant could barely tolerate this man—and that only for his influence or his wealth.

"You have been long in this country, Centurion," said Gaius. "You know these things, no doubt. I buy only for beauty's sake and yet a part of beauty is authenticity. Price does not matter. This exquisite little statue. My friend says it is from Alexander's time and certainly it has the Greek sweetness to perfection. So gentle. Really I love it." He had the statue in his soft white hands and raised it and kissed it with tenderness, his eyes closed.

"And yet I think not of Alexander's time," he said, passing the statue to the centurion. "But made perhaps by one of Joseph's Jewish craftsmen in Antioch. What do you say, Centurion?"

In receiving the statue, the centurion caught a whiff of rose perfume from the tribune, warm and womanly, but did not know whether it came from his hands or from the dark curled hair with six tiny ringlets across the white forehead.

"I do not know about these things, sir," said the centurion. "But no Jewish craftsman would carve this, for they are forbidden to carve images."

"Oh come, Centurion," said the tribune. "Perhaps not a Jewish craftsman then. But some other. Have you not yourself seen several other pieces like this around?"

"No sir," said the centurion.

"Why do we concern ourselves with it, Gaius?" said the merchant. "You love it. It is yours. Love is not subject to price."

"Ah, but you put me in your debt beyond my ability to pay," said the tribune. "Truly you enslave me by your generosity." But the tone of the words was offhand and cynical and, having gained the statuette, the tribune put it negligently aside with other gifts or purchases and continued with his examination of the goods of Joseph of Antioch. The centurion could not for a while discover the reason for his own presence. Plainly he had been wrong in thinking that the tribune wanted to discuss his report. He decided the tribune wanted to make use of his own knowledge of the merchandise of Judaea so as to bargain shrewdly. But the tribune soon showed that he was capable of very shrewd bargaining himself, and, although he pretended that money was of no importance, he always managed to extract some gift from Joseph when he agreed to a price which he had protested was too high.

When he had finished with his purchases, he had his slaves undress him, and then walked in a loose cloak to the bath of his villa where he plunged nude into the scented water and invited Joseph and the centurion to join him, though he well knew that Joselph of Antioch, being at least nominally a Jew, could not do such a thing without being defiled. Joseph refused but the centurion was obliged out of respect for his senior officer to accept the offer. He started to strip him but then had to suffer the slaves to disrobe him. He had the country Roman's dislike of nakedness in the presence of others and retained his cloak until he was about to step into the huge bath, when he was compelled to surrender it to a slave, a Canaanite girl of fifteen or so, who took the robe and eyed his hard muscled body with frank interest.

"Ah, ha," said the tribune. "You like the old stallion."

The girl smiled and gave a toss of her long hair and then, still holding the robe, ran a small soft finger down a scar which extended just below the chest of the centurion across his torso to above the left hip. It was the remnant of a terrible wound, and in knitting the muscles had been shortened so that the centurion leaned slightly to his left, though this was not noticeable when he was clothed.

"You were nearly made a god," she said, and laughed.

"The arena?" asked the tribune with some enthusiasm. Occasionally soldiers were given permission to fight as gladiators for prize money or because an officer had made a bet on them, though these fights, privately managed, were never permitted to go to the death, as were the contests between the true gladiators.

"Britain," said the centurion.

"On the shield side?" asked the tribune, and the barb was not lost on the centurion, for on those rare occasions when Roman troops were demoralized and put to flight, they threw away first their heavy shields, so that a wound on the shield side was a sign of cowardice.

The centurion, despite himself, glanced quickly at the white soft unscarred body of the tribune and said nothing. The look was not lost on the tribune. "Mine are wounds of the spirit which can never be healed," he said.

"You will dine with us tonight," he continued. "A small company. Joseph, yourself, Pilate and I. And you may have Asthar to wait on you"—nodding to the Canaanite girl—"I will surrender her for the night."

"I thank you for your kindness," said the centurion. "But if it is permitted, I would prefer my own servant."

"You have one?" said the tribune. "Fair and young?"

"An old man," said the centurion.

"Really? How interesting. I have heard indeed that there is pleasure in them. How old is your favorite?"

"You mistake me," said the centurion. "He is my servant. I do not know how old he is."

"Come. You must be able to guess," said the tribune.

"He has no age," said the centurion, thinking of the blue tribal markings of Ruafocus which dedicated him and his people to the deer. "He is of a people and so has no age." The tribune looked at him and then at the Canaanite girl, and for a moment it seemed to the centurion that the tribune was afraid.

CHAPTER SIX

The centurion had not time to return to his own quarters after the bath, for Pilate would be arriving any moment and it would be lacking in courtesy if he were not on hand to wait on him. He sent Ruafocus, who during the afternoon had been sitting in at the atrium of the villa waiting his master's call, to his quarters to get fresh clothing. The tribune offered a pallium and toga of beautiful Egyptian manufacture, but these Longinus declined because he was not entitled to a toga and was old-fashioned enough not to presume to wear the garment reserved by tradition for those of equestrian rank. He preferred the knee breeches, short kirtle, and red cloak of the legion.

He was nervous, not looking forward to the dinner, for he was a man of the camp and not used to participating in the social entertainments of his superiors. In any case he took no pleasure in eating, though politeness would demand that he make a show of partaking copiously and with relish of the multitude of dishes that would be served. As a young man he had drunk heavily whenever he could. Now he drank sparingly, and knowing that his empty cup would be kept filled at the banquet and he would be expected to acquit himself in the consumption of wine, he had Ruafocus bring him an ounce of olive oil which he swallowed to line his stomach against the effects of the wine to come.

Pilate arrived with a large escort. There were at least twenty with him, advisers and secretaries and personal servants and among them his wife Procula. She was a plain woman, of medium height, plump and with heavy features which might have given character to a man but in her made a cruel joke of the attentions of her beauticians. Her eyes were small and the dark dye under the lower eyelids, intended to give them allure, only made her small eyes look piggish. Her face and neck were freckled, and cosmetics, mostly the white paste used to give a look of delicacy and even sickness, could not cover these. They showed through and the attempt to hide them made them only more obvious. Her hair was dyed not red but ginger and, though her own, had all the appearance of a wig clumsily contrived. She wore it in the Greek style, swept up from the neck into a pile of curls at the back, but the curls looked like a sheep's wool and this upward style revealed a slight mound of fat around the back of her freckled neck, rather accentuated by her round and overlarge shoulders.

As soon as she arrived, carried in a litter, Gaius greeted her at the gate, lavish in his attentions though annoyed by her presence, which changed the character of the evening the tribune had planned. Pilate was amused by the setback to the tribune's plans, and to avenge himself the tribune conducted Procula around his villa, pointing to his treasures and asking her opinion of various objects knowing that she had no knowledge of them and the questions could only embarrass her. She tried to carry off the role of a wife of the procurator, a woman of travel and knowledge and influence, but the attempt was miserable. She was one of the plebs and though her family had wealth, it had been gained by thrift and commerce and she had no background of culture.

"I showed her a necklace of Hassim of Corinth—four hundred years old and quite unique—and she said, 'We have something like that at the palace,' " the tribune told his friends later. Afterward the phrase "We have something like that at the palace" never failed to raise a laugh at the expense of Pilate's wife.

The dinner was but a little delayed by the arrival of so many unexpected guests. The tribune's steward had anticipated such a turn and ordered food in abundance, but Pilate, while his wife was being shown around by the tribune, summoned the centurion to his side to question him before the meal. He dismissed his secretaries and led Longinus into the garden to a small knoll on which was a toy temple to Cybele. The temple was not really a place of reverence but part of the collection of Gaius Servius; a testament to his taste rather than to his devotion to the goddess. There was a bench of yellow and black marble before the temple, and here Pilate sat and motioned to the centurion to sit beside him. It amused Pilate that even when he was seated the centurion looked as though he was at attention. Pilate knew the man well and valued him as an officer though he was sometimes troubled that having been long in Judaea the centurion might be losing the Roman point of view. That was one of the problems of occupation duty—to obtain officers who knew the local situation intimately without their sympathies being involved.

"A few matters in the tetrarchy of Herod concern me,"

said Pilate. "The Levite you found. What do you make of him?"

"He was not killed by robbers," said the centurion. "I think he was killed by enemies—a Samaritan perhaps or a Syrian."

"He had been sent secretly from the Temple to the man called John, I am informed," said Pilate. "Very secretly. For that reason he took the road through the swamps rather than the other through the higher land. Did this prophet called John mention him to you?"

"No. All that passed between us is in my report. But perhaps you have not read it . . ."

Pilate silenced him with a gesture. "I have read it," he said. "Beyond what you say in your report, what do you make of this John?"

"He is like the others," said the centurion. "He talks of being the herald of the Messiah."

"The herald of the Messiah," said Pilate. "That is what interests me. The others claimed to be the Messiah himself. This one is content to claim an inferior role—that of a messenger. Do you see the significance?"

"No," said the centurion.

"It suggests an organization—a gathering of forces to support this Messiah who is to come." He looked keenly at the centurion. "One man Rome never fears," Pilate said. "An organization is another matter. Have you seen any sign of an organization being formed tending to disobedience or revolt?"

"The Essenes," said the centurion. "But that is purely religious at present."

"Have you heard whispers of any organization called 'The Sons of the Father'?"

"No," said the centurion.

"Then watch for it," said Pilate. "I am told such an organization is in the bud." He paused and then said abruptly, "What do you know of Barabbas?"

"Barabbas?" repeated the centurion. "It is said he is a Galilean. But I have heard also that he is from Peraea. He is a brigand, posing as a patriot. His object is booty and his own enrichment."

"But he has a band of as many as two hundred, armed," said Pilate. "A nice little nucleus. Think of the name. Barabbas. Filius Patris. 'Son of the father.' Do you begin to see something now, Centurion?"

"You speak, Excellency, of an organization inimical to Rome linking Barabbas, John and this Messiah?"

"I speak of the possibility of such an organization," said Pilate. "If it exists it may not necessarily aim at Rome. But if it aims merely at civil disturbance, that is Rome's concern. I think it aims at the Herods. They have no favor with the people in the country. But the family of Herod is closer to the people of Judaea than you or I can ever get, being Gentiles. This Messiah agitation is of long standing and of particular concern to the Herod family. Remember how seriously Herod the Great took the matter. Hearing that an infant born in Bethlehem thirty years ago was to be the Messiah, he slaughtered all the infants in the neighborhood. And that was before he went mad. He did it when he was sane and that he did it at all, risking tremendous unpopularity, shows how seriously the House of Herod views this Messiah movement among the Jews. We Romans hear these rumors of Messiahs among the people and dismiss them as part of the Jewish madness. We would do well to take them seriously."

"It would be possible to remove John," said the centurion. "If that is your wish, I can have it done readily."

"Leave him," said Pilate. "If he is to be arrested, let Herod arrest him and then Rome will not be blamed. Concern yourself rather with Barabbas. Watch for a connection between him and John, but do not move against him without my order. What do you think of the new tribune?"

The question about a senior officer, far above him in rank, left the centurion without an answer.

"Come," said Pilate. "Rome asks. Not I."

"I scarcely know him, Excellency," said the centurion. "He is a young man of greater authority and lineage than I."

"He has spoken against you," said Pilate. "A gift would be in order."

"From me?" said the centurion. "I have no gift."

"That is the trouble. You hold the lucrative post at Capernaum and have no gift for him. Still perhaps you were of service to him this afternoon in his bargaining with Joseph of Antioch."

"No, sir," said the centurion. "I was of no assistance."

"None that you know," said Pilate smoothly. "But the presence of the senior centurion at Capernaum on such an occasion, would, I assure you, be of great assistance. I fancy our Gaius came out well in the exchanges. You do not take bribes, I hear?"

The question, lightly put, shocked the centurion. "No," he said. "They have been offered, but I have refused them. I am accused . . . ?"

"No. You are not accused. You are known even among your detractors to be honest. Continue to be so. The tribune wishes you removed from Capernaum but I will protect you as long as you remain honest. Do not assume from this that I admire honesty. It has its uses, but so have subterfuge and deceit, and many of those around me I have selected for their excellence in these virtues. But at Capernaum I need a plain man such as yourself. If at any time at Capernaum you are offered a bribe that is irresistible, take it and let me know. I will not punish you but will remove you from Capernaum.

"One word of advice. Watch yourself at the banquet tonight. Remain sober and observe. Do not take any forward part in the talk." He paused. "I will contrive to see that you are seated near my wife," he said. "You may converse with her without fear. In return, do not press spiced apples on her. She cannot resist them and suffers afterward from a grippe." He paused. "You and she are of a kind," he said. "She is of the country."

The centurion, thinking the interview over, rose, standing before Pilate and waiting for the word of dismissal.

But instead of dismissing him, Pilate returned to the main topic of the interview. "Concerning the Levite," he said. "If you find further news of the slayers, send it secretly to me—direct. You should know this much about the man. He was sent, as a result of certain whispers, to see John. He was to find out privately whether he was himself the Messiah. You will understand that had he answered yes, his death would have been contrived by the priests at the Temple who sent the Levite. They do not want a Messiah of obscure origin, coming from nowhere. They don't want an imposter, in short, because the inevitable disturbance would weaken their authority over the people and weaken their position with Rome, which has been liberal to them in all matters of religion.

"If John denied that he was the Messiah and said, as he now says, he is but the messenger of the Messiah, then the Levite was to find out who was the real Messiah. And he also would die. And yet it was the Levite, traveling secretly, who died. What do you make of that?"

"His errand was known," said the centurion.

"Exactly," said Pilate. "And that being so, our simple wilderness prophet has ears in the inner councils of the Temple. A conspiracy then. Better entrenched than we might have suspected. It was a mistake, however, to kill the Levite. For that exposed the conspiracy. Better for John to have seen him and lied to him."

"Prophets cannot lie," said the centurion simply.

Pilate looked at him surprised and then said, "Yes. That is their biggest handicap. Experience should have taught these Jews to muzzle their prophets and work in silence. But then, they insist that they are led in everything by their god which, in view of their state, makes inevitable the conclusion that their god is a fool—or dislikes the Jews."

CHAPTER SEVEN

The dinner consisted of numerous courses, richly spiced; many of the dishes were cooked in Greek wine with its strong flavor of resin. The eating utensils were spoons, knives and hands, and since each item of food was laden with its own sauce, making for messy eating, each guest was provided with an outer robe to put over his garments to prevent staining. A slave stood behind each guests to wipe his face, hands and chin as required, and basins of water were brought when needed so that the hands could be washed when they became too greasy.

The tribune, Gaius Servius, stuffed himself at every course that was served, thinking nothing of leaning over the table to cut a strip of fat and flesh off a roast piglet, or spear with his knife a couple of doves.

The guests were seated at tables arranged in a horseshoe, with Gaius at the center of the bend of the shoe, Pilate to his right, and Procula to his left—the centurion being seated to the left of Procula. Joseph of Antioch was to the right of Pilate, and the other guests—Pilate's staff and friends of the tribunes—were along the two arms of the horseshoe, so that sixteen or eighteen in all were seated at the table. Gaius pressed Joseph of Antioch to try some of the roast pork, which, of course, he could not do, the pig being an unclean animal. When he refused the tribune twitted him on the matter, asking whether his god exercised a stewardship over his belly, and Joseph had to suffer this mockery for he could not leave without offense to both the tribune and Pilate. The centurion now found that the tribune got some of his pleasure out of mocking others and grew uneasy wondering what particular mockery was in store for him.

Food was served from behind each guest, rather than from the center of the horseshoe, for this area was reserved for the entertainers of whom there were as many as the dishes. They were not particularly impressive—singers, dancers, and tricksters who produced eggs from the ears of slaves, and smoke from bowls of flowers. Yet they served to provide a focus of attention and discussion for the guests and, together with the wine, eased the reserve which had been among them.

The piece that produced the most enjoyment was a mock gladiatorial combat with two small apes dressed as gladiators, but armed with clubs rather than swords. They each had tiny shields and wore little sandals. The company was helpless with mirth, for before the combat the mimic gladiators removed the sandals and flung them away, one landing in a bowl of soup and splashing the guests. They were chained lightly to each other so that they could not get away and their combat consisted of frantic dashes about, dragging and entangling each other in the chain and battering each other with their shields which, strapped to their arms, they could not discard. One was finally knocked unconscious in this panicked show and the other dragged him around, chattering and screeching. Then he turned to examine his fallen comrade, went instantly into a fury at being still tethered to him, and started to belabor him so hard with the shield that in a short while the victim was dead. The victor was then crowned with a little wreath of laurels though he had to be held by his trainer while this was done. He then defecated and made water at the same time out of sheer fright, amid shrieks of laughter from the company, and even the centurion found it amusing.

What followed could only be an anticlimax. There was a harpist and a singer and a Negress who did a dance with a constricting snake as her companion, but when it came the turn of a poet to recite an ode, accompanied by music, and dealing with Jove and the delights of Olympus, the tribune dismissed him, summoned the musicians and let his guests amuse themselves with their own conversation.

The centurion had little small talk himself, but was relieved to discover that Procula, made less self-conscious by the wine, was talkative and all he was required to do was listen to her. Her talk did not greatly interest him but required no comments. It dealt with spells and magicians and dreams and their interpretation. She asked him in what month he had been born and on what day and said she would have her astrologer cast his horoscope. She told him that because of his birth date, the hour between seven and eight in the morning was especially malevolent for him and he should avoid any important actions at that time.

"I know this because your birthdate comes one day before Pilate's," she said, "and the time of malevolence to which we are all subject each day, is one hour later according to the day. So for Pilate the dangerous hour is from eight to nine and I have begged him not to hold court at this hour. But he ignores me for he does not believe in these things."

At this time Procula had been only a year in Judaea, for she had not come out with the procurator when he was appointed to the position four years previously. Being comparatively new to the land she, after a while, questioned the centurion about the Jews, their customs and beliefs, and her questions and comments were at one and the same time simple and cunning.

"I am told that they hate us," she said. "And yet I do not find any great hostility in their attitude. What do you think of them?"

"They are not hostile to Rome," said the centurion, "because Rome has not interfered with their religion, but has given them every facility to follow their beliefs. As you know, Herod the Great built the temple in Jerusalem and for that they were genuinely grateful to him. But they resented the placing of the Roman eagle on the wall of the Temple and when that was done, Herod became more unpopular than if he had refused to build the Temple in the first place."

"That is what is so curious about them," said Procula. "Wasn't the Temple built with the help and sanction of Rome? The eagle but acknowledged this. It was right that the people should know who had given them the Temple."

"It is a matter of religion," said the centurion. "Their god commanded them not to carve any images. So the eagle carved on the walls of the Temple is a violation of their god's commandment. Herod would have done better to leave the eagle off. It was a small thing to Herod but a big thing to them."

Procula shrugged. "I think it nonsense," she said. "If

their god didn't like the eagle and was a true god, he would knock it down. But he doesn't, so plainly he isn't offended. Can you speak their language?"

"Yes," said the centurion.

"Then you are able to talk to them intimately. Why do they have only one god?"

"That I don't know," said the centurion. "It is just so with them. They believe they are the sons of their god. It is that belief that unites them despite all their differences."

"They say they can work miracles—some of them. I have heard there is a pool in Jerusalem which a spirit strikes every day, and whoever is first in the water immediately afterward is cured of any illness. Have you seen the pool?"

"Yes," said the centurion. "Before being transferred to Capernaum in Galilee, I was often on duty at the pool. We have to have a guard there to keep order. People thrust and wrestle and fight to get to the water's edge and many are hurt and some of them killed. Once one of our men secretly threw a pebble into the pool to ripple the water as the spirit does, and two hundred of the sick and crippled flung themselves into it immediately. When the trick was discovered, the soldier was nearly torn apart and he had to be scourged to appease the people."

"Have you seen any real miracles at the pool—people cured?"

"Yes," said the centurion. "I saw a child cured of blindness and another of being dumb."

"Could you be sure that these were miracles?"

"Reasonably sure," said the centurion.

"But have you ever seen a miracle yourself—happen right before your eyes?"

"I saw a man get water from a rock in the desert," said the centurion, and told her of his meeting with John.

"I am afraid of the Jews," said Procula. "They have secret knowledge and secret power. They never laugh. I think that is what makes me most afraid of them. I get the feeling that they are all joined in a conspiracy against us. I wish we had never come here; that Pilate had never sought and received this appointment. We were happier at home, among friends."

"After a while you will come to understand them better," said the centurion. "Then you will come to respect them and like them."

"I could never like them," said Procula. "They have not the normal appetites of men—games, eating, drinking and women. Pilate can find no mistress among them. What of yourself, Centurion? Have you succeeded where Pilate has failed?"

"No," said the centurion. "I have no Jewish mistress nor any other."

"Then how do you content yourself?" asked Procula.

"There are women among them, as among all people, who are available. The law condemns it, and the penalty is death by stoning. But in the country places, the law is not strong and the people more natural."

"What a miserable god theirs is that keeps watch on the stomach and the bed," said Procula. "He is more devil than god, denying under terrible penalty all natural pleasures."

"There are other pleasures," said the centurion. "I have occasional glimpses of them."

"Where?" asked Procula.

"Among them. And in their synagogue."

"You have been in their synagogues?"

"Only in the area in the outer court reserved for Gentiles. There is something there—a peace I have not found elsewhere."

"I have heard it said that they have great orgies in their synagogues and that is why the Gentiles are not permitted inside."

"That is not true," said the centurion. "Unless you can call reciting and chanting their prayers together an orgy."

"I don't understand them," said Procula.

"That is why you fear them," said the centurion.

"You do not think them a great danger to us?"

"In themselves, no," said the centurion. He thought for a while and added, "It is their god who is a great danger to us. They would die for their god. So long as we do not offend him, they will remain subservient."

"I think you have become half a Jew yourself," said Procula.

Longinus had been so involved in the conversation with the procurator's wife that he did not notice that a silence had fallen on the company and Procula's remark was heard by them all.

"Dearest Procula," said Gaius. "You do the centurion an injury. I have heard indeed that he is called the Jewish centurion. But I know his loyalty to Rome for he bears a wound—though on the shield side—suffered in the cause of Rome. Come, Longinus. Defend yourself. Tell us how you came by this noble scar—on the shield side."

Trapped, the centurion turned from the company to look at Ruafocus standing behind him. The old servant was partly in the shadow and the muting of the light around him lessened his years so that he seemed younger.

The centurion turned again and, fixing his gaze on an oil lamp that flickered on the table before him, commenced his story.

CHAPTER EIGHT

The day had been one of intense, moist heat, which was not disturbed by a whisper of wind so that the men of the maniple, when they were but an hour on their way, were already sweating heavily. On the march they were of course forbidden to talk, but they usually contrived to grunt or cough or make some sound which was a form of communication between them. An experienced officer knew that a little noise among the men meant that they were in good spirits, but when they were utterly silent they were tired and surly. They were surly now and made no sound other than their own labored breathing and the cadenced thump, already a little ragged, of their heavy sandals on the ground.

The maniple was not at full strength. It was, what the name implied, a mere handful of men—twenty in all—and in charge not of a centurion but of a senior soldier. It was returning to the camp at Sarum, ten miles distant, having been on a surveying expedition in connection with a plan for a military road between Sarum and the fortification built on the river at Win. For the greater part of its length, the route lay over rolling plains, covered with a very rough grass with here and there a small copse of trees on top of curiously shaped hills which were avoided by the Celts as being burial grounds of chieftains. The soil of these plains was thin, no more than an inch deep, and there were areas where the subsoil of chalk showed through, white as snow. Over these chalk areas, there was a shimmer of heat. Longinus could remember these shimmering chalk areas well. He had seen nothing like them in either Italy or Gaul and they seemed to add to his thirst and to the intolerable weight of his armor, for the men of the maniple had been required to march fully equipped.

They wore helmets and leather cuirasses, terminating in skirts of leather flaps which hung just short of the knees, and carried javelins, short swords in their scabbards, shields, and, swinging from belts around their waists, bags containing a sponge soaked in vinegar and water which was their drinking supply. The maniple should have been accompanied by four horsemen as outriders and scouts, but, the distance to Sarum being but a day's march, these had been dispensed with. That there were no horsemen made the soldiers nervous, for they felt naked without them and although Rome controlled its forts at Win and Sarum and Londinium and other places, the countryside of Britain was still unconquered and would remain so until a network of military roads had been cut through it.

Longinus, though in his first term of service with the legion, had several years of soldiering behind him. He shared the nervousness of the other men over the absence of cavalry. Out on the heat-stricken, rolling plain the maniple was utterly exposed, watched by a pitiless sky and by a pitiless eternity of land around. When the men were on the brow of a hill, they could see for ten miles around. When they were in a valley, they wondered what lay over the brow of the rise ahead of them. An army could have been hidden in one of these valleys. The sense of being watched was overpowering. That they were watched soon became evident.

Figures no bigger than ants appeared singly on the plain, sometimes on the horizon, sometimes nearer between them and the horizon. The figures were mounted and kept the little huddle of Romans in sight except when they went for a short time into the depths of one of the valleys. There were occasional distant horn notes, thin and melancholy as the cry of curlews. Without orders from Fuscus, the senior soldier, the men increased the length and rapidity of their stride as the sun rose higher. Safety lay for them in Sarum and Sarum was some miles off. To camp on these terrible plains at night would be to be exterminated.

Fuscus commanded by reason of seniority rather than of intelligence. He was all bone and muscle—a big head on the shoulders of an ox—and he had once, in a rage, when working with the farriers, picked the two feet of a cavalry mount off the ground and thrown the animal on its side, whence he earned the nickname Fuscus Luctator Equi—Fuscus the Horse Wrestler. Certainly his strength was enormous and he liked to pretend that he was a descendant of the god Hercules, and on his sword he had put the sign of the god, ignoring the fact that Hercules, when he used a weapon at all, used a club.

Between Fuscus and Longinus there was some rivalry, for Longinus, though lacking the strength of the horse wrestler, had a quicker mind, a better education and equal courage. This rivalry showed itself only in that Fuscus could not conceal his resentment of the younger soldier on occasion, jibing at his schooling and intimating that any counsel he gave in matters that concerned them all was based less on wisdom than on cowardice. Yet sometimes he took the advice of Longinus and when it turned out to be good, he was jealous rather than grateful, and assigned him to latrine and other unpleasant camp duties. Longinus bore this in patience, for even as a youth he had control of his temper and because he did not show resentment Fuscus concluded that he was afraid of him.

When they had been some three hours on their way, the linc of march always rising slightly, they crossed the brow of yet another hill and saw before them a steep valley at the bottom of which lay a little wood perhaps half a mile in breadth but extending three or four miles in length. The trees were thick and of great variety—oak, beech, fir, ash and clm—so that the wood was not of one shade of green but of many shades according to the kinds of leaves.

A small stream led down the valley headed from north to south and running through the wood, which was surrounded on the near side by an area of thick bracken flowing up the side of the valley toward the maniple.

Sighting the wood, Fuscus called a halt to debate whether the maniple should risk plunging through it in a direct line for the Sarum encampment, which lay four miles or so beyond. The wood was an obvious place for an ambush, but to skirt it, to either the north or south, would add two hours to the march so that it would be twilight or more probably dark before the safety of the camp was reached.

"Well," said Fuscus, "what shall we do? These horsemen have been keeping an eye on us from a distance and I have no doubt that if we go around the wood, they will, as the day wanes, attack us in the open. So few men can scarcely defend themselves against an attack in the open by cavalry. Particularly if they have chariots, which I do not doubt they have hidden from us behind the hills.

"On the other hand, if we enter the wood, they cannot use their horses and must fight on foot. Furthermore in so thick a growth they will not be able to use their javelins and in hand-to-hand combat, we may, the gods willing, survive."

Nobody made any comment on this. As soon as the halt had been called, the men had cast themselves down on the ground, utterly weary. The absence of an immediate reply irritated Fuscus and he called on one or two of them by name for comment, but they only shrugged, leaving the matter entirely to him.

"And you, Longinus, what do you say?" asked Fuscus.

"We are plainly going to be attacked," said Longinus. "So it is no longer a matter of reaching Sarum but of preserving ourselves until it is realized at Sarum that we are overdue and a force is sent out to relieve us. We should therefore encamp on the most suitable ground and wait. After dark a man could be selected by lot to try to get to Sarum and report our situation."

"Encamp in the open?" said Fuscus. "Twenty men? It is plain that you have not got the making of a centurion in you."

"We do not need to encamp in the open," said Longinus. He pointed to a knoll to the south of them on which stood a growth of trees. "That is one of their old burial grounds," he said. "They are afraid of those places. If we encamp on top of that we need not fear their cavalry, and the steep sides of the mound will give us the advantage should they, overcoming their fears, decide to attack."

"And what of food and water until help comes?" asked Fuscus.

"We carry an extra day's ration," said Longinus. "We are not unused to hunger and thirst. We can last out three or four days by which time help will certainly arrive or all will be lost in any case."

Some of the men thought this a good plan and supported it. Had it been put to a vote the plan would have been carried. But Fuscus could not relinquish the prospect of reaching Sarum in three hours if they were but bold enough to plunge through the wood at the bottom of the valley.

"In such a place," said Longinus, "we will, without a doubt, be ambushed. We will not be able to fight in any order for the wood is thick and I have no doubt the bracken grows heavily all through it. We will have to fight every man for himself and, losing the strength of cohesion, all will be slaughtered."

"I agree that the wood is an obvious place for an ambush," said Fuscus. "Indeed it is too obvious. It is plain to me that they wish us to skirt the wood as a trap, when they can attack us in the open with cavalry. Therefore the wood is the safest route. On your feet, then, and follow me. And if any of you are carrying extra or unneeded supplies, dispose of them for we will not need them when we reach Sarum."

Some of the men then drank up the whole content of their sponges and, having eaten all the hard bread they needed, threw the rest away. But Longinus took only enough liquid to refresh his mouth, knowing that when the stomach is full any wound is much more grievous.

"If we are ambushed we should have a plan," he said before they started. "We should perhaps divide into two bodies of ten men, sending one ahead and letting that get clear of the wood before the other starts. Then if one part is attacked, the other can come to its aid."

But Fuscus would not hear of any division and mocked at the plan for dividing so small a force in the face of the enemy. Nor was the plan supported by the rest of the men of the maniple, whose whole training was to fight as a body and in as large a body as possible. All being decided then, they set off down the valley toward the yellow-green bracken that spread before the wood like a sea at the base of a cliff.

This bracken was at first small, scarcely coming to the knees, and the ground below it rocky. It was thick enough to conceal the rocks so that the men stumbled and, stumbling, cursed and made a great deal of noise. Farther along, on the approaches to the wood, the bracken grew higher, so that in places it was up to their shoulders and the sweet smell of the sap surrounded them as they thrust their way through, leaving a train of broken ferns behind them. Certainly theirs was not a secret approach, and nearing the first of the trees, which were growths of hazel nut, Longinus warned Fuscus again that they were walking into an ambush.

"How do you know?" snarled Fuscus. "You can see through the trees?"

"Not a single bird has come up from the woods despite all our clamor," said Longinus. "Plainly there are men inside."

Fuscus was shaken by this observation but judged it too late now to go back. He thrust into the growth of hazel, thwacking the slim trunks mightily with his sword and so, with his great strength, cutting a way for the others to follow.

The men came after him but in single file, for they could not now keep any military order. A moist quiet descended on them when they had penetrated the edge of the wood to find a thick undergrowth not of bracken but of rhododendron. The ground was a foot or more deep in soft mold so that their feet made only the slightest rustle in walking. The rhododendron was thicker even than the bracken and they had to thrust and hack their way through the clumps, some of which covered an area of half an acre and under whose low-growing branches a thousand men could be hidden. Still they found nothing, and stumbled, thrust and slithered down the valley to the small stream which flowed through the length of the wood. The stream had cut a little bed for itself. It was only five feet wide, but its banks were four feet or more deep and treacherous, the edges being heavy with rotting leaves. Because it was too wide to be crossed by a single leap, the men had to slither down the bank, ford the stream, and attempt to climb up the moldering sides beyond, which crumbled under their weight, tumbling them back into the stream.

Since they found that the opposite bank could not be climbed by a man armed, each put down his pilum or throwing spear and his shield, and, carrying only his sword, strove to get out of the riverbed. Longinus was one of the first out and was turning to help another when there was a blast of a horn, so near and harsh as to turn him for the moment to stone. There came then another blast and then another. Then from all parts—from both banks and from up the river and down the river—a horde of Celts flung down on them, some of them even dropping out of the trees overhead, and without any prospect of making a formation for defense, such as a shield circle, the men of the maniple were compelled to fight individually for their lives.

His shield and javelin being in the riverbed, Longinus and those with him had to defend themselves with their swords against the spears and war axes of the Celts. Instinct and training drew them into a little circle in which at least they could protect each other's backs. But their foes were too many and in a matter of less than a minute Longinus was alone and he himself cut down by a blow from a boneheaded ax which, catching him a little forward of the right shoulder, laid his chest open to the ribs in a slash which ended slightly above his waist—on the shield side.

"I twisted from the blow," said Longinus, "and did not know I had received so heavy a wound, for I fell in the soft loam when twisting and rolled over toward the riverbank but felt no pain. However, when I tried to rise I was in one instant, from the flexing of my muscles, completely drenched with blood which spurted through my breastplate so that it was plain that the river of my life would soon be spent.

"Knowing myself nearly dead, I managed to get to my knees and looked for my sword so that I might lean on its point and be done with life more quickly and so not see the slaughter of my comrades. But my sword was gone and I collapsed again to the ground, falling forward and in such a position that I could see what was taking place in the riverbed where most of my comrades were trapped, for all on the bank had now been killed."

"You watched?" asked Pilate quietly.

"Yes, Excellency. I watched, for I wanted to see whether Fuscus was indeed, as he pretended, of the loins of Hercules. On that, his last day, he had certainly something of the god about him. Being still in the river, he had not parted with his shield and fought from behind this like a giant, and was the last of the maniple to go down. Indeed, the rest were already dead or dying, several having drowned, being pinned to the riverbed both by the weight of their armor and by the javelins thrust through them. Fuscus then alone remained bellowing like a bull and laying about with a fury that compelled the admiration of the Celts. He slew several and at last, when he was utterly surrounded, they signified that he should surrender, whereupon they would spare his life. Indeed, they would not even attack him, and when he rushed at them with his sword they defended themselves but by some agreement would not thrust back at him, for I think they had concluded that he was indeed a god.

"He was in great anguish at being refused a soldier's death by his enemies and at last, ceasing his attacks, threw down his shield, tore off his cuirass and, exposing his chest, begged his fores to thrust a spear through him. But either because they thought him a god or because, which may also be the case, they reasoned that such a fighter would be of great aid to them if he would join their cause, they refused him death. Whereupon the Horse Wrestler, still standing, reversed his own sword and thrust it three times into his belly and then fell forward on the mound of those he had killed and so died.

"He died well," added the centurion. "The best of any man I have seen die. It was the full glory of death for such a man as he."

"And you?" asked Pilate.

"Encouraged by Fuscus, I made one more effort to die by my own hand though I believed death very near in any case. I could see a sword a little way from me but just beyond my reach. I crawled to it and was about to grasp it when it was kicked away and I was raised up by the tribesmen to find myself facing the chief of the tribe who had launched this attack."

"And who was he?" asked the tribune.

"He who stands behind me now as my servant—Ruafocus," said the centurion. All eyes turned on the aged Celt, and it was Pilate who broke the silence.

"But Rome conquered," he said. "And he who was once your captor is now your slave."

"My servant," said the centurion. "I would not enslave such a man as he. Indeed, were he to accept Roman citizenship, to which he is now entitled, he would be my comrade. But he will not, as he says, desert his own people."

The others, a little drunk, showed signs now of wearying of the story and would have left the matter there, but the tribune wanted to know more and asked how and for what reason the centurion's life had been saved by Ruafocus and how he had come at last to be his servant.

"That may be quickly told," said the centurion. "The chiefs of tribes among the Celts are elected, though it is not rare for the office to pass from father to son in this way, though not by heritage. Ruafocus had no son but only a daughter who was not married. Having seen how well the men of the maniple acquitted themselves, and Fuscus, whom he would have preferred, being dead, he decided to save me and have me nursed back to health so that I could wed his daughter according to their rites and sire a son who might one day be chief of the tribe.

"At the back of his mind too was the thought that a Roman son-in-law could instruct his people in the warcraft of the Romans and would so be a very valuable addition to his tribe. They are skilled in the treatment of wounds and sewed up mine with deer sinew and dressed it with mosses and so it healed and the wedding was arranged, for I was helpless in the matter, being taken by them into the western reaches of the island where there was no Roman camp nearby.

"I remained with the tribe two years, planning to escape but biding my time until we should be close to a Roman encampment or there was news of a legion close by. Eventually this opportunity arrived. My wife, whose name was Una, suspected my plans and, when the time came for me to steal away, she discovered me and threatened to raise an alarm so that I was forced to slay her.

"I reached a cohort of the Tenth Legion which was encamped fourteen miles away and so was returned to the service of Rome." The centurion glanced at Pilate and said dryly, "For the time of my captivity I received no pay. But my knowledge of the Celts, their language, their customs and religion and methods of going to war was of such value to the legion that I was soon promoted to the rank of centurion and so had my reward."

"You loved this woman?" asked Pilate, ignoring this.

"I loved Rome," said the centurion.

"And about Ruafocus—you were able to persuade your commander to attack the tribe to avenge the slaughter of the maniple?"

"No," said the centurion. "He had treated me well. I wished him no harm. His own people, however, demanded that he attack the legion because of the death of his daughter at my hand. He was powerless to resist this demand without forfeiting his position, and the attack was made and repulsed, because of my knowledge of the ways of the tribe. Indeed the tribe itself was exterminated except for a few who escaped. Ruafocus was captured and brought to me to dispose of as I wished."

"So you made him not your slave but your servant?" asked Pilate.

"Excellency," said the centurion. "Let him answer. There will be no loss of dignity in it, for though he is now old, yet he was a soldier once as are you and I."

"Answer then," said the procurator to Ruafocus.

"He owed me a life," said Ruafocus. "Many lives—the lives of all my people as well as my daughter."

"And so you bargained for yours?"

"No," said Ruafocus. "I told him that he owed me a life and if there was any justice before his gods, he should permit me to stay with him as my debtor until he had paid me back that life which he owed me."

"You hold then," said Pilate, "that you are entitled to kill the centurion at any time and without punishment?"

"That would be the Roman way," said Ruafocus. "You believe that one death cancels out another because you deal in death. A death for a death does not give back a life. It is a life that he owes me. That I must have from him."

"And how is he to give you a life?" asked Pilate.

But to this Ruafocus made no reply.

BOOK II

CHAPTER NINE

When the first graying of dawn began to outline the hills on the Peraea shore of the lake, the fisherman Peter woke his two partners, James and John, and told them that they would make one more cast of the nets. They were sleeping forward in the cuddy of the boat, an area by the bow which was decked over to provide some shelter, and they were cold and stiff and loath to go to work.

"It's no use," said John. "You know it's no use yourself. The storm has frightened the fish and they have gone down too deep for the nets. It will take an hour to set them; another hour to haul them in and we'll get nothing for our troubles but Jordan weed."

Of the two brothers, James and John, John was the talkative one and whenever there was anything to do he took a negative attitude toward it. The two had very quick tempers, even for Galileans, and so had been given the nickname Sons of Thunder because they were likely to erupt at any moment.

Peter didn't reply to John. When the time came he knew he would work the nets anyway, but his nature demanded that he object first of all. Peter was standing in the stern of the boat, leaning on the steering oar, weary and stiff himself for he was worried and had scarcely slept that night. They had already made three casts of the net between dusk and midnight without catching more than two or three eels which were worthless, being unclean. Then the storm had come—one of the sudden tempests that swept the Sea of Galilee at that time of the year—and they had put into a small cove and anchored there.

Peter was wet through and shivering and for a moment he was weary of his boat and the net and the sea and the wind and all things connected with his trade. He was weary because he had worked as a fisherman for twenty-five years and fishing still provided him with only an uncertain living. His wife was dead, he had no sons or daughters, and in twenty-five years more he would be no further ahead than he was now. If he got a good catch, the tax collector was there at the landing place in Capernaum to assess the value and demand his share for the government. He could save nothing. Keeping the boat and nets in repair took any little surplus he could put by, and then there were whole weeks when the weather was too bright or the wind from the north, when he got no fish at all. Then he had to borrow money at ten percent from the Gentile money lenders and so the whole self-devouring process went on. Now, because the mood was self-defeating, he shook it off and went forward past the mound of net amidships to help James get up the anchor.

The anchor was a circular stone with a hole through the middle which in the soft bottom was sufficient to keep his beamy, light draft boat secured. Once free of the mud it was easily raised and Peter went back to the steering oar, calling to his two helpers to get the lateen sail on her for there was a little wind out of the west they could use in setting the net. The yard of the sail had been left hoisted, so all that was needed was to loose the brails that pulled the sail up to the yard like a blind, and set the sheet. When this was done, the boat slipped south on the west wind and James and John started feeding the net over the side into the dark and still almost invisible water.

In taking it in, they had piled it in a hurry so that several times it tangled and James blamed John for the tangle and John blamed James; the two brothers were always quarreling in this manner.

"Do you see Andrew's boat?" asked Peter, ignoring the quarrel.

"He went back to Capernaum," said John. "There are never any fish after a storm anyway."

Peter knew this to be usually true. But he was stubborn. He never liked to give up. He had to make one more try with the net to satisfy the stubbornness in him. The wind came in a little stronger and that cheered him. He would be able to make the whole cast with the aid of the wind without having to take an oar with James while John fed the net overboard.

He turned the boat eastward, called out to the others to watch for the jibe, and put the steering oar over in the direction of the wind. The big lateen flopped to the other side of the boat and so he continued, sailing her in a huge circle which, when completed, would bring the two ends of the net together. But just before he completed the circle the wind dropped anyway, so that they had to take to the sweeps to bring the boat around and gather both ends of the net. And then they started hauling it in, foot by foot, looking for fish and shaking out the weed.

The eastern mountains stood out quite plainly now against the lightened sky, and across the lake they could see the warm glimmer of a light or two in Capernaum.

There were no fish—only river eels and these were flung back into the water with curses. When they had the net back on board, the sun was up. James looked at the mound of the net full of weed which would have to be washed when they got it ashore. Then he looked at Peter and he felt sorry for him.

"We could try again," he said. "There's a little wind. We could make another cast."

"No," said Peter. "The net has to be washed. The boat has to be cleaned. We need to rest and eat. We will try tomorrow."

"It is God's will," said James.

Peter made no reply.

They reached Capernaum at ten in the morning and instead of going to the pier where they docked, pulled up on a beach to the south where they could wash the net in the water, which was the first task ahead of them. As they approached this beach they saw a crowd of people on it, gathered around a man with fair hair who was addressing them. The crowd pushed so close around him that only those close by could see him or indeed hear what he was saying.

"Who is it?" asked Peter.

John, busy at his sweep, turned to look over his shoulder and said, "I'm not sure. I think it is the young rabbi from Nazareth. I hear they threw him out of the synagogue and were going to push him off the cliff."

"Why?" asked Simon.

"Blasphemy," said John. "Something to do with interpreting a passage from Isaiah. We should go farther down the beach away from the crowd."

"No," said Peter. "Pull in where he is. We can listen to him while we wash the net."

They grounded the boat behind the young rabbi, who

had his back to the water. He turned as the boat came in and looked directly at Peter and said, "Help me on board. The crowd presses about me and cannot hear what I say."

Peter, however, hesitated, for it was not in keeping with the dignity of the rabbi to come aboard such a boat as his on which Gentiles and even Samaritans had been carried across the lake. The rabbi, a stranger, did not know of this and would lose prestige if he boarded the boat, for Peter himself had not an unblemished reputation in Capernaum.

Seeing him hesitate, the rabbi said, "Come. Will you not help me?" and reached out a hand. Peter then helped him up to the bow of the boat, to the little deck that formed the cuddy. When he had done this, Peter went quickly to the stern of the boat, to be as far away from the rabbi as possible so that people could see for themselves that there was no association at all between himself and the young doctor. When he had got to the stern, Peter pulled a mound of the net over to him and started picking off the weed, throwing the cleaned net into the water to James and John, who were washing off what could not be picked off by hand.

In the stern of the ship Peter could not be seen by the crowd on the shore and above the mound of the net amidships could only catch a glimpse of the back of the rabbi's head and shoulders, and this obscurity comforted him. Peter took off his rough cloak and, clad only in a loincloth, went ahead with the work, listening to the words of the rabbi but with his head bent for he felt that he could not look at the rabbi without being disrespectful. The words of the rabbi came to him at times clear and at times indistinguishable when his voice was carried off by a little flurry of wind. He was surprised to find that the rabbi was not expounding the law and its interpretation and this relieved him greatly, for when it came to the application of the law, Peter, in common with many of the Galileans, was a backslider and thought nothing of fishing on the Sabbath or gutting his catch, which was even worse.

"Do not go to the synagogue or the Temple to pray or offer any prayer to your Father if you are angry against your brother or against any man," the rabbi said. "Think of this. How can you expect the blessing of your Father in Heaven if you yourself are angry with others? How can you expect love and compassion when you yourself harbor hate and enmity? You cannot have light and darkness in the chamber of your soul for one must overcome the other and the two cannot exist side by side. Therefore forgive your brother, put aside your enmity, and in this is prayer itself and the work of your Father will be shown in yourself, his child, and you will receive his blessing in abundance.

"Do not be quick to accuse others, lest your Father be quick to accuse you and his accusation will be far more grievous than your own. You do not see into other men's souls but only into your own. Therefore cleanse that which has been put in your charge and of which you have knowledge. The good housewife cleans her floor and sets her beds in order and keeps her hearth free of ashes that she may live in comfort and without strife. But this is just the contentment of the body which must die and corrupt. How much more important it is to cleanse the hearth and the floor of the soul, which is the abode of God, and sweep out of it all dross and corruption, that it may be a fit place for your Father.

"Listen to what I say. When you take your clothes to wash them in the river, pounding them on the washing stones, rinsing them and pounding them again until they are as white as snow, reflect as you work on the cleanliness of your soul, whether it does not more greatly need pounding and scouring and rinsing than the garments on which you labor. For only those whose souls are as shining garments of honesty and charity and compassion will see their Father and the others will be turned away."

The next words struck particularly hard at Peter. "How many of you," the rabbi said, "will labor all day and all night without gain, and yet will continue to labor in the hope that there will be a little gain for you at some time, even if it be only one drachma which is soon spent. Yet you will not labor one tenth, nay, one hundredth part so hard in the work of your Father, for which the reward is certain and will last forever. Do you then not believe in your hearts that your Father will reward you? Why then do you call yourselves the children of God? What father is there who will not reward his children for the work they have done which is according to his will? Reflect on what I have said for I give you the way to salvation which I have from my Father. Those who heed my words will be glorified by men and those who do not heed will be mocked by men for all time. So let it be."

When the rabbi had finished Peter remained bowed, working on the net, but thinking of what had been said. He was determined not to show himself until the rabbi had got ashore, for it would be unthinkable for him to go near the rabbi, who would soon discover from others what kind of man he was and would rebuke him. So he stayed quietly in the stern of the boat and then, feeling a shadow over him, looked up to see the rabbi standing beside him.

He moved back a little, away from the rabbi, and the rabbi said, "Peter—put out from the shore and let down your net for a draught of fish."

Now it was the custom among the rabbis, both of the Sadducees and of the Pharisees, when they made use of someone's premises to talk to the people, to make a little donation to the owner in thanksgiving. Peter thought that the young rabbi wanted to do such a thing, but being without any money, for he seemed very poor, proposed to make payment by having him cast the net, when whatever chance fish he caught would be taken as the rabbi's offering to him. But it was plain to Peter that this rabbi knew nothing of fishing and did not know that with the sun up, no fish would be caught in the net and the rabbi would then be disgraced. So to protect the rabbi from this further loss of dignity, he said, "Master, there are no fish. We have labored all night and have caught nothing."

Peter looked in the rabbi's eyes when he said this, striving to convince him by the look that he was not being disrespectful but only trying to protect him in a matter of which he had no knowledge. But the rabbi's eyes were calm and suggested a smile not of superiority but of sympathy. Seeing this Peter said, "Master, because you have told me to do so, I will make another cast of the net."

He turned to James and John but they had heard what was said and were already in the boat. It struck Peter as strange that they did not even argue with him, for he expected an argument from the two brothers who were always opposed to doing what was asked of them in the first instance. Far from being unwilling, they were cheerful and did not quarrel with each other though half the net was in the water and half in the boat and there was plenty of room for quarrel here as to who should bring it all aboard. James pulled in the net and John took one of the sweeps and pushed the bow of the boat off until the vessel was afloat.

Peter, ignoring the rabbi for a moment, looked about to see whether there was any indication of fish on the lake, such as birds flying over the water or a ripple on its surface, but saw nothing. There was no wind either, so he took a sweep and told John to take the steering oar and they worked the boat a little way from the shore. When they were in thirty feet of water, though still within hailing distance of the beach, Peter glanced at the rabbi, but receiving no signal from him, started to let the net overboard.

There was a little current at this place, the edge of the Jordan flood which was stronger in the middle of the lake, and he thought that perhaps a fish or two might be taken in the current, though not enough to justify the labor of putting the whole net out. Still, he started to feed the net over the stern and decided to let it all out, which would give a better chance of catching something and saving the rabbi's dignity. He had got out no more than twenty feet of it, however, when there was a quick flurrying of the still water which was churned to white on the surface.

"Fish!" cried John. "Look at them! Thousands of them!" He dropped his oar and with James started to fling the net in bundles over the side to get more of the fish. These came from all sides, hurling themselves into the net, some of them so determined to be entangled in it that they leapt out of the water so that the whole surface of the lake about them erupted fish in a vigorous joyous multitude. The noise they made was like the heaviest of thunder showers. The fish struck the net so hard that they dragged it from the boat, and the net was soon all overboard and pulsing with fish whose gleaming sides turned the water to molten silver behind the boat.

James and John struggled to get the net in, their voices high pitched with excitement, and they shouted to Andrew, whose boat was ashore, to come to help them for the net was bursting with fish and two men could not handle between them a yard of it because of the weight of the catch.

But when Peter saw the host of fish, he stared at them in amazement, and then groaned and threw himself at the feet of the rabbi and, not daring to look at him, said, "Lord, depart from me, for I am a sinful man."

But the rabbi touched Peter on the shoulder and, raising his head, looked at him with love and said, "Follow me, Peter, and I will make you a fisher of men."

CHAPTER TEN

Peter was the leader of the fishermen who kept their boats at Capernaum although most of them lived at Bethsaida at the point where the Jordan flowed into the Sea of Galilee. He was the leader not because of agility of mind but because of a stubbornness and stability of character, a contrast with the quick spirits of the others. He did not speak much and then only when he had spent a great deal of thought on a particular problem and heard everybody else's point of view. His decisions were not brilliant but sensible and of benefit to them.

It was Peter, for instance, who had organized the fishermen who traded at Capernaum into a loose cooperative. They pooled their catch and each boat drew a share so that there was often a small fund available from which individual boat owners could borrow rather than having to go to money lenders who charged a heavy rate of interest. This cooperative provided a tax benefit, for the tax on the pooled earnings of all the boats was less than if each boat paid taxes individually, and the individual boat owners were protected out of the common fund from being penniless on days when they caught nothing.

The financial management of this cooperative had for a while fallen on Peter, but he did not like the work and he had found a sort of treasurer for them all in Judas of Kerioth, who lived at Bethsaida although, unlike the others, he was not a Galilean or a fisherman. His profession was that of a money changer, an essential occupation in a land which had half a dozen systems of coinage. He was honest and astute enough to see that Peter's cooperative of fishermen could supply him with a good fee in return for handling its financial affairs. He could do what they could not do—argue with the tax collectors on the current value of coins, and see that no more was paid in the way of taxes than was absolutely necessary. Indeed Judas of Kerioth, charging one percent of the gross for his services, earned his fee many times over, and whenever, the common fund being exhausted, money had to be borrowed, he could find a lender at reasonable rates.

Originally Peter had been co-owner of a boat with his brother Andrew, and it was Judas who had pointed out that if Andrew owned his own boat they could draw two shares from the common fund and have twice as much claim on its credit.

Peter did not like to be separated from his brother in this manner, but the proposal of Judas was but common sense and in no way dishonest. Peter also considered that Andrew was younger than he, and might one day marry and have a family of his own when he would need a greater income. So the brothers had parted as joint owners, each having his own boat, though they remained very close to each other. Andrew was not as reserved as Peter. Life had not soured him in any degree. He knew Peter better than any of the other fishermen and knew that his silence, far from being a sign of strength, was the result of an agony of indecision and self-doubt and an inner loneliness that could not be banished.

When, after the great catch of fish, the boat, almost sinking, had been nursed to the fish dock to unload, a big crowd was on the dock, for the news of the catch had spread rapidly through the town and many had closed their business to see the fish for themselves.

Peter left the docking of the boat to James and John, and when the rabbi stepped ashore the crowd fell silent and parted to let him by, many bowing their heads. Peter followed him, at a little distance, stopping only to snatch up his cloak to cover his nakedness. They went through the crowd without a word but when they got to the edge, Longinus, the centurion, who had been away in Caesarea, stopped Peter and said, "What is all this confusion about? Why is everybody here?"

"Leave me," said Peter. "I follow the rabbi," for he was afraid of losing sight of him. He pushed by and the centurion shrugged and, clearing the way through the crowd, found the two boats loaded to the gunwales with fish so that they were almost sinking. Several boats set out immediately from the dock thinking to get a similar catch and James and John and Andrew, sending to their homes for bins of salt they had there, set about the task of scaling, gutting, and salting the catch lest it should spoil.

Ruafocus was with the centurion for he followed him everywhere and, hearing the crowd shouting the Greek word "miracle," he asked one what had happened. This man said that the heavens, at the bidding of the rabbi, had opened and poured a shower of fish right into the boat, and indeed a lot of them believed this though the story was plainly foolish for part of Peter's net was still over the side, folded in a bag and full of fish.

"The Lord has sent us a great prophet and he will deliver his people, Israel," said the man, who was in a kind of hysteria and started making high-pitched, wordless noises like a dog, which disgusted the centurion, who hated to see any man lose control of himself. He pushed the man aside roughly and stepped from the dock to the boat. James and John stopped their work to glare at him, for the centurion represented Romc and they resented Rome's interfering in this sacred matter.

"How did you come by all these fish?" asked the centurion.

"There is something wrong about it?" asked John, bristling immediately. "There is a law now about how many fish a boat can land at Capernaum?"

"There's no law about how many fish a boat can land at Capernaum," said the centurion with a touch of menace. "But there is a law about creating a public disturbance. Now, what happened?"

"We put out our net at the command of the rabbi," said John. "There were no fish. None anywhere. And as soon as the net touched the water the whole surface of the lake was alive with them. We didn't have to trap the fish, making a bag. The fish came from all around and flung themselves into the net. They were so thick in the water you could have walked on them. They did this because of the rabbi."

"What rabbi?"

"The rabbi from Nazareth," James said.

"What did he call himself?" asked the centurion.

The two brothers looked at each other. "He didn't say."

"He is called Jesus, the son of Joseph the builder at Nazareth," said one of the people in the crowd.

"You know him?"

The man looked uneasily at the others around. He did not like to give information concerning a fellow Jew to the centurion, a Gentile. "There are stories about him," he said. "When he was twelve he went to Jerusalem with his parents for the Passover. He stayed there a week expounding the law and he confounded all the doctors of the law with his answers to their questions. But he was too young to be made a rabbi at that time."

"And since then?"

"He remained home with his parents. His father is dead."

"He was not his father," said another. "He was his foster father."

"The woman had been married before?" asked the centurion.

"She was visited by an angel who told her that she would conceive a son by God himself. The rabbi is that son," said another.

The centurion had learned to listen carefully to the stories of the Jews for often, even in their wildest tales, there was something worth knowing to be found. "So he is the son of God," he said softly.

"So it is said," said the man who had volunteered this information.

"The Messiah?" he suggested.

But to this nobody made any reply.

It was important to discredit any rumors concerning a Messiah immediately. "Isn't this the same rabbi that was thrown out of the synagogue at Nazareth for blasphemy?" the centurion asked. They said nothing. "It is strange that the son of God should be thrown out of a synagogue," he said. "Now go about your business. The fishermen have been lucky. That's all. These swarms of fish are not unknown." He looked at a boy in the crowd who had a withered arm, a not uncommon defect among the Jews, and said, "If that boy had been aboard when the fish were taken, you would have attributed the catch to him. Fish are fish. No man knows their habits and their moods."

"That is true," said John. "No man knows the habits of fish and no man can command them. But the rabbi did. And I know he did because I was there and I saw what happened and you were not there. So attend to your own affairs, Centurion, and leave what belongs to the people of God to them. Not even your Caesar, with all his armies, could produce such a catch as this."

"You keep a civil tongue or you will be in trouble," said the centurion. "As for Caesar, let me remind you that he commands men enough to catch all the fish in this lake, drain the lake dry and turn your Jordan River to flow into the western sea." With that he left them, but he was concerned over the excitement that this strange catch of fish had aroused. He needed to know a great deal more about this rabbi from Nazareth, and particularly whether there was any connection between him and the prophet who was called John the Baptist, and Barabbas, the robber.

When he got back to his quarters, the centurion told Ruafocus to summon certain people among the Jews, among them one Bar Timeus, a blind beggar who regularly supplied him with information. They were to visit him that night.

Peter meanwhile still followed the rabbi, who had left Capernaum and was walking along the road to Bethsaida across the river. Peter did not, out of respect, speak to him for some time, but reflecting that the rabbi had not likely eaten anything that morning, he finally summoned up his courage and suggested that they visit his mother-in-law's house in Bethsaida and she would prepare a meal for them.

To this the rabbi agreed, but when they were approaching the house, a servant, who was standing at the door, came hurrying to meet them, half running but incapable of going faster because of her long robes.

"Your mother-in-law is near death with a fever," she said. "She does not know me but calls out your name over and over again. She is in great need of you." And then, as if all this was Peter's fault, she said, "Why are you late? Why did you choose this day of all days to be late? I have been waiting at the door for you since sunrise."

"Rabbi," said Peter. "Wait a little. I must hurry to her."

"Lead me to her," the rabbi said.

The house was a small place and rather neglected. Some of the outer plaster had fallen off the walls exposing the dark brown mud bricks below, and the courtyard, kept scrupulously clean in other houses and pleasantly shaded with citrus, was, in this house, used as a storage place for tubs holding fishing lines, boxes for packing fish, cork floats for nets, and other gear. Peter had many times determined to clean these things up, but found himself always either too tired or too busy.

As with all the other houses of Palestine, there were no interior sleeping quarters in Peter's house for it was the custom, except in the short winter, for all to sleep on the flat roof. A flight of steps by the side of the house led up to it. When it was necessary to sleep indoors, because of weather or sickness, then the light pallet bed was placed in a corner of the general room, sometimes in a little raised alcove where the sleeper was less likely to be disturbed by the lambs and kids which were often allowed in the shelter of the house in foul weather.

Peter's mother-in-law, whose name was Susanna, was lying on her pallet in such an alcove, with a curtain of sackcloth drawn across to give her privacy and a little quiet. Entering the house, Peter was for the first time conscious of its disarray and its variety of odors—of tar and fish and damp and rancid oil (for he could not afford to buy the best grade for cooking) and of the heap of pots by the hearth, not put on their shelves but stacked there and testimony in themselves to the gravity of the illness of Susanna, who was very conscientious about keeping her hearth tidy. One of the pots contained some broth which had been warmed during the night for Susanna, and there was now a glistening skin over the surface of it. Susanna's day clothing was thrown on a stool, which she herself would never have permitted for she had some shelves built in a corner in which all clothing was neatly folded when not in use.

All this disarray troubled Peter. When he had put aside the curtain which served as a door and taken in at a glance the neglected state of the interior of the house, he turned to the rabbi with a look which contained a plea to delay a little while outside until order could be restored. But the rabbi, first pausing to say the prayer of blessing before entering the house, went in and without a word made his way past the litter to the sleeping alcove and gently pulled aside the sackcloth curtain to reveal the sick woman on the pallet.

The fever which had seized her was so intense that

lying on the pallet she shivered as if freezing, making the pallet itself tremble. Her eyes were shut and her lips parted and they had a purple tinge to them. Her face had the sunken aspect of one dead, and seeing her so, Peter forgot all else and flung himself down by the pallet and took her hand between his own, huge by comparison, and held it as if by his very grief and love he would pour strength into her body from the great strength he had himself.

"Peter, Peter," said the rabbi. "Do not grieve. She will not die." Then he took the hand which Peter was holding and said, "Woman, I say to you, arise."

Immediately the trembling stopped, the sunken cheeks were filled, the lips were no longer drawn back in a purple grimace and the woman sat upon the bed, looking strangely young so that she resembled her own daughter who had been Peter's wife. She looked at Peter with concern and said, "You must be hungry and here I lie sleeping. You have been working all night and return to find me not yet awake."

Then she turned to the rabbi and said, "Holy One, I saw you coming in my sleep. My house is poor but I will make my heart a palace for you to live in, and you who can see into the heart know that this is so. Blessed am I, the least of the daughters of Israel, that you have come to me and to my son, for no king, born or yet to be born, has received such a treasure as we who are the least worthy."

"Daughter," said the rabbi, "because you have loved God, so also he loves you and you shall see him face to face in the glory of his tabernacle and with his angels."

Peter was so overcome with awe and gratitude and love for the rabbi that he could say nothing. He could think of only one thing to do. He had put aside an especially large fish, which he had smoked himself and which he had intended to take to the Temple in Jerusalem as the ritual first offering of the fruits of his labor. But he had had some misgivings about this, for the fish was of a rare kind of sturgeon whose roe would fetch a very good price if sold and he had hesitated between giving it to the priests at the Temple, where it would be lost among a lavish multitude of gifts and thus scarcely noticed, and selling it to the servants of the steward of Herod who would pay a handsome price for it—well above what would be available in the market.

But he did not hesitate now. He took the fish from the peg on which it hung, picked up the earthenware jar with the roe and brought them both into the house. He thrust fish and roe at Susanna and said, "Prepare these for the rabbi. Let the very best we have in our house be given to him." He turned to the servant who had backed into a corner and had the hem of her robe across her face in fear and said, "Woman. Get the best of oil that is to be had and bring it for the rabbi's food." And then he remembered that he, though the head of the house, had not even offered the rabbi water to wash his feet, which was the custom. So he got a bowl and filled it with some of the water of purification which stood in a large jar just inside the door and, kneeling before the rabbi, took his feet, which were small and delicate, in his hands and washed them himself.

While he was doing this he was filled with a great happiness and contentment of mind such as he had not known for many years and he said, "Rabbi, I will follow you wherever you go, and I will bring my brother Andrew, and James and John and all who know me. And we will guard you and tend to you and see that you want for nothing, for all that we have or are able to obtain and every breath that we draw will be yours."

The rabbi said, "Is all this for a few fish and because I cured her whom you love?"

But Peter said, "Rabbi, we are poor and sinners and yet you have come to us."

CHAPTER ELEVEN

On this occasion the rabbi stayed a week at the house of Susanna, and during that time Peter would hardly leave his presence. A sleeping booth was erected for him on the roof and although he might have slept in the house, the time being winter, the rabbi preferred to sleep in the open. He had a deep love of nature so that he not only preferred to sleep in the open but also to eat in the open and spent much of his time in the small plot of land, cultivated as a garden, which was behind the little courtyard at the back of the house.

All homes had such gardens to provide vegetables in season for the household, the work being done by the younger members of the family. In Peter's case, Susanna tended the garden and it was laid out in plots with onions, white cabbage, carrots, artichokes and other vegetables which in the mild climate would produce all year around. It was a pleasant place, surrounded by a mud wall, painted with a whitewash made from the powder obtained by burning the shells of shellfish, and this coating gave a smooth finish like pottery to the wall along which honeysuckle and roses had been trained to grow. There were two fig trees in the garden, barren now because of the season, and an olive tree which had been planted at the time of Peter's marriage. It was the custom to plant an olive tree at a wedding and its fruit was the property of the progeny of the marriage, for the olive of all the trees of Israel was the most loved. It was the symbol of both peace and fruitfulness and so great was its bounty that one tree of good growth could support a whole family from the sale of the oil. The rabbi loved this tree which in a quarter-century of growth had an abundant foliage and produced a good harvest of olives each year.

"How silent and uncomplaining it is, and yet all its works are good," the rabbi said. "Storm or drought, still it stands performing the task given it by the Father, faithful to the seasons and putting on no show of splendid flowers to evoke the admiration of men, but contenting itself with silent benefits. It gives of its abundance, asking no payment. Neglected, it will still produce its harvest. Blessed is the olive which shall be known to all men of all times and all nations as that which produces only good. I tell you that the olive shall stand higher in the regard of men, even among those who do not know the Father, than the mightiest kings of earth."

After the morning prayers, announced by the blowing of a ram's horn and the cry "Hear, O Israel . . ." from the synagogue, the rabbi would work for a while in the garden, weeding and watering and thinning out those plants which overcrowded the bed. Susanna had, in a clay pot, a small rose which, despite all her care, produced only small warped blossoms. Seeing how ruthless the rabbi was in rooting up poor growths she asked him to spare the rose and indeed suggest anything that could help it.

"It is sickly and yet I love it," she said. "I have given it my best care though it hardly thrives. But it still tries to live and I cannot throw it on the fire."

Peter was indignant at his mother-in-law for bothering so great a man as the rabbi with her sickly rose and rebuked Susanna saying, "Woman, this is no matter for such a man as the rabbi. You should be ashamed to mention it." Susanna blushed and had difficulty not bursting into tears of shame at the reproof from her son-in-law in the presence of the rabbi.

But the rabbi said to Susanna, "In the tenderness of women lies the strength of the nation, and without it no nation may endure. Woman, lay your hand upon the rose in love and it will blossom for you. For out of love comes the true nourishment and that from which love is withheld must die."

Susanna then went to the rose and touched the small stem and felt it quicken in her hand. The leaves which had been curled and brittle filled out green and strong. The little branches which had been dry at the end and dead were nourished with sap and in the center of the bush a white rose grew, long-stemmed and beautiful as a carving of ivory. She brought the rose, trembling and speechless, to the rabbi and the rabbi said to Peter, "That which is most lost, needs most love."

That was the second miracle that the rabbi performed in the house of Peter's mother-in-law, but it had a strange effect on Susanna, for that evening she became ill with a weakness so that she had to lie on her bed and Peter was concerned for her. But the rabbi said, "Do not be troubled, Peter. She has given of herself and has been weakened by it, but her Father, who has seen her love, will restore her." The next day she was well again.

Many people came to the house when they knew the rabbi was there and the wonders he had done, but they were afraid of him, for few of them observed the Law in all its details and indeed many of them did not know the

Law. They realized that because of this they would be condemned on death to the outer darkness. They were emboldened to come only because they knew that Peter was one of them and they tried to convince themselves that since the rabbi was staying in his house he would not spurn them and tell them not to approach him, as others did, because they were unclean.

They were, of course, all Jews and made the sacrifices required at the Temple and journeyed to Jerusalem for the Passover. But they did not keep the Sabbath strictly, often working on it to make a little money, nor did they set aside a corner of their tiny fields for the use of the poor, nor leave on their olive trees the unripened fruit to be picked later as the gleanings for the poor. Once when the collectors from the Temple had come for the tithes and had been determined to take a jar of oil which belonged to a widow, and was indeed her sole possession, they had driven them out of the town and created such a commotion that the centurion from Capernaum had had to come with his soldiers to put down the disturbance.

Longinus had sided with them and had told the collectors that the Temple was rich enough and to be on their way. This was a shameful thing, to be protected by a Gentile from the officers of the Temple, and they had been angry with the centurion for interfering—more angry with him than with the men from the Temple. Since they had brought shame upon their religion they took the oil from the widow and gave it to the Temple officers and turned on her for withholding from God that which belonged to him, and told her that her misfortunes came from this attitude.

Thereafter they had avoided her as one who had brought a scandal on them and later driven her from the town. She now lived in some unknown place in the hill-sides. After dark she came into the town to see what scraps she could find to eat. But it was known that she was a witch and the children were frightened of her.

The people then came to the house but stood outside in the evening when their work was done and the rabbi talked to them, though they stood some distance from him at first and, if he moved toward them, they moved away.

They soon discovered he was not one of the Pharisees or of the Sadducees, for he rarely quoted from tradition or the Torah, but spoke about their own lives and the Father, as if the Father was still on earth and not in the Temple in the Holy of Holies but among them, like a familiar companion.

After a while they started to bring gifts for the rabbi. They did not give these directly to him, being afraid that the gifts would not be worthy, but they left them by the outer wall around the house when they had gone—sandals, jars, platters, lengths of cloth from their own looms, a goat, a few doves, fish, oil and small amounts of flour.

Since it was dark when they came they carried torches which lit a face here and there but left many of them in obscurity. At first they stood while the rabbi spoke to them, but after a while, when one or two of them had been bold enough to sit, many of them sat on the ground, having first of all put their gifts by the wall to the right-hand side of the gate.

Now one evening the widow, thinking she would not be discovered, came to the edge of the crowd and listened to the rabbi and the next evening she brought a gift for him, but it was so small that she was perplexed as to what to do with it, for if she put it on the ground with the other offerings, it would soon be lost. Among these offerings was a handsome water jar which she knew would have to be washed and purified before use. Therefore, when no one was looking, she slipped her gift into the bottom of the jar, knowing that it would be found there after the purification. But she had hardly done this before the rabbi stopped in what he was saying and said, "Let her who has placed the mite in the jar come to me."

The widow tried then to run away, lest she be humiliated for making so tiny an offering to the great rabbi. Her very efforts to get away, however, flitting like a mouse in her rags along the white wall against which she could be seen in the starlight, were her undoing. The potter who had brought the jar caught sight of her, and she was seized and brought before the rabbi where, trembling, with the torchlight held over her so that she was not even given the mercy of shadow but exposed to them all, she fell in shame to the ground and pulled the rag of her cloak over her head.

"Daughter," said the rabbi, "stand now before me and uncover your face."

But she said, "Rabbi, have pity on me. Do not command this of me."

"I have pity and do command it," said the rabbi quietly.

Then she got to her feet and moved the cloak away, and those holding the torches shrank back in horror. For her nose was thickened and her face had become swollen and there were shiny nubs of flesh over her eyebrows which were the marks of leprosy.

"Daughter," said the rabbi, "why did you give me the mite?"

"Rabbi," she said, "my heart told me to give it to you and I hoped that in the purification of the jar the mite itself would be found and purified and so be wholesome. But I have sinned, and therefore let them do with me what must be done."

Now the penalty for a leper coming among those who were clean was death and some immediately looked around for stones with which to dispatch her.

But the rabbi said, "Let no one harm this woman. She has been tested by the Father and all her afflictions have not destroyed her faith or her love."

Then, while the others held back in horror and thrust their children behind them, he threw the cloak off the woman's head and put the palms of his hands on her diseased face and looking to heaven said, "Father, in that she has loved so much, let her be cleansed." And when he took away his hands the woman was cleaned of the leprosy and her face was beautiful.

Now the woman was a proselyte, that is, a convert to the Jewish faith. Her parents had been Greek and her name was Veronica, which means "the true image." From that day she followed the rabbi.

CHAPTER TWELVE

James and John of Zebedee and Andrew, Peter's younger brother, had stayed close to the rabbi in the week he was at the house of Susanna, and they knew of the miracles that he worked there and determined that he would not be parted from them. The enormous catch of fish had been sold, a tenth of the price sent to the Temple officers, the Roman tax paid and a further tenth given to Simon, the rabbi at Capernaum, for distribution to the poor.

All this financial transaction had been handled by Judas of Kerioth, who had effected the sale through his contact with Hana, who was the steward of Herod Antipas and did all the purchasing for the Tetrarch's household. Judas was eminently just in these transactions and took the tenth for the poor out of the gross receipts, rather than after the deduction of the Roman and Temple taxes. He made a special point of telling Simon, the Capernaum rabbi, of this and pointed out that the offering for the poor taken from the gross represented thirteen and one-half percent and Simon praised him and cited his example to others.

Judas was glad of the praise, for people distrusted

money changers, a profession which it was held could breed only dishonesty. He was sensitive about his reputation, disliked the hard looks he got in the course of his business, and craved the respect and indeed the affection of his fellows.

"Who deals in money has no friends," he said to Peter. "None trust me or love me. If I am invited to dine with a family, it is not for myself that I am asked but for some advice concerning exchange or investment. I love the law and the beauty of the law. And yet all people talk to me only of money."

Peter felt sorry for Judas and brought him to the rabbi and praised him for the work he had done for them and the honesty he showed in all transactions. "He is a good man, Rabbi," said Peter. "He will change even the smallest of coins of the poor for the Temple offerings and at a generous rate. He has advised many and asked no fee."

"What do you say of yourself, Judas?" asked the rabbi.

"Lord," said Judas, "let me stay with you."

"Judas," said the rabbi, "I will not forbid you to follow me. But consider the reason why you do so—whether it is to gain esteem among your fellow men or whether it is to serve the Father."

"Rabbi," said Judas, "with all my strength I wish to serve God."

"If," said the rabbi, "this is indeed so, Judas, then your salvation is assured." Judas then took all he possessed and gave it to the poor both at Bethsaida and at Capernaum and he was greatly praised for this work. He decided that he would have nothing more to do with his profession and, when a man greatly in debt came to him and asked how best to settle his accounts with his debtors so that he would not be imprisoned and his farm seized,

Judas sent him away without advice. "I have nothing more to do with these matters," he said. "For I follow the rabbi of Nazareth and he is not concerned with such things."

When the man had gone he felt disturbed that he had not advised him, but decided that his concern arose only out of trying to break with the habit of giving such advice. The man was imprisoned and his wife came to Judas to plead with him for help. "You are well known," she said. "If you will speak for my husband to his creditors, he will be released. He is not a bad man but foolish and extravagant and loves to spend on his friends what he has not yet earned. If you would speak for him, your word would be a bond for him and he would be released to me and his children."

But Judas was irritated by the foolishness of the man in money matters and said that the punishment he was now suffering was what he had earned for himself. "Let the friends on whom he spent the money help him," he said. "It is no concern of mine. Furthermore I do not believe what you say, for the man's farm cannot be taken from him and he himself be put into prison."

"The farm was taken from him by his creditors," said the woman, "but he has been imprisoned for failure to pay the tax to Rome."

"Then see the tax collector and plead with him but not with me," said Judas and dismissed her.

The woman then went to the tax collector of the Romans, whose office was at Capernaum to one side of a heavy gate which stretched across the landward end of the passenger and freight jetties in the town. The gate was in two parts, one for foot passengers and one for goods brought on donkeys or camels or in hand carts. None could pass through the gate from either side without first paying tax on any goods they had which were for sale either in Galilee or in Peraea across the lake.

Some called this the Gate of Sorrows and some the Gate of the Flies, not only from the large number of flies which gathered around the donkeys, camels and goods which stood waiting to pass, but also because among the Jews the Romans were called "the flies" because they were everywhere and gorged themselves, without politeness, on everything.

When the woman got to the office of the tax collector it was noon, and such a crowd of people were waiting and all of them bad-tempered that her heart failed her. Nonetheless she waited patiently, thinking that when this crowd had been dealt with, she might see the tax collector, whose name was Levi. But the office was shut at four in the afternoon, though many of the people had not been passed, and these were compelled to miss boats and wait until the following day.

She had left her own children at home and was anxious for them. There were several families there with children, who would now have to spend the night by the gate. Many of the children were crying, their fathers beside themselves with frustration and anger and the mothers fretful, both scolding the children and comforting them. They had taken their places in line so that when the gate opened in the morning, they would be served in their proper turn. But when anyone went away to get food or water, his place was often usurped by those behind and so quarrels and fights broke out to the amusement of the Roman soldiers on duty, for they liked nothing better than to see the Jews (always quarrelsome, in their opinion) shouting at each other.

Thinking of her own children, the woman went to the well which lay farther along the waterfront and brought a bowl of water to give to the small children in the line. She refilled the bowl many times and brought water, though this cost her her place in the line and she would now have to go to the very end. Standing with the soldiers there was an old barbarian with a long thin face and long white hair like that of a horse's tail. He frightened her because on his face there were blue marks such as the Gentiles put on their faces to mark themselves as the sons of Cain and therefore of the devil. He watched her bringing the water, and his very age and the fierceness of his looks increased her fears.

After a while the barbarian went to her and said, "Your heart belongs to the People of the Deer."

"Why do you say this evil thing to me?" she asked, drawing back into the crowd.

"There is no evil in it," said the barbarian, "for among the People of the Deer, of whom I was once a chieftain, the mother of one child is the mother of all children. And so I say that your heart belongs to the People of the Deer for you feel for the children of others and bring them water. Why are you here? You have no goods. You could have passed the gate earlier."

"It is for my husband who is imprisoned for tax," said the woman. The others, hearing that she was in trouble with the tax collector, drew a little aside, even the ones to whose children she had brought water. They did not want to be identified with one who had trouble with the officials of Rome, for they had enough concern of their own.

"I will see what I can do for you," said the barbarian. He went to the door of the tax collector's office, before which stood a soldier, and, ignoring him, opened the door. A little later he came out and, telling the woman to follow him, led her into the office. Inside was the collector of taxes and a centurion.

"Sirs," said the woman. "Forgive me. I came here at the bidding of this man. I did not intend to intrude in your business."

"What is your trouble?" asked the centurion, looking angrily at the barbarian. "State it quickly."

"My husband is imprisoned for nonpayment of tax. I came to ask that he be released so that he can hire himself out. Our farm has been taken from us for debt, but the tax will be paid out of his wages."

"What is so special about this case?" asked the centurion, not of her but of the barbarian. "Every woman's story is the same. Their husbands will always pay taxes if they are released from jail. Yet they neglected to pay them beforehand."

"She gave water to the children and lost her place in the line," said the barbarian as if this explained everything.

"And that pays the tax?" demanded the centurion sarcastically.

"Roman," said the barbarian, "you also have a debt unpaid."

The centurion stared at the man and then said to the woman, "How much does your husband owe and what tax is this?"

"It is the land tax," said the woman. "We have five fields and the tax is six pieces of silver for each field. Thirty pieces of silver."

The centurion looked at the tax collector and said, "I will pay the sum myself."

"If you want to free the man, I can remit the tax out of my fees, with no cost to you," said the tax collector.

"Do your own good works. Don't appropriate mine," said the centurion gruffly. He turned to the woman. "Your husband is held here in Capernaum?"

"Yes."

"See that he is released," he said to the barbarian. The woman seized his hand and kissed it and the centurion said wonderingly, "So much for thirty pieces of silver?"

CHAPTER THIRTEEN

The rabbi, at the end of the week, told Peter that he wished to go into the wilderness to the east of the Jordan to fast and pray and that he wished to be alone to commune with the Father. Peter wanted to go with him, and John of Zebedee, who especially loved the rabbi, pleaded to be allowed to join him. These two men were quite different in their characters and perhaps that was the attraction between them, for the rabbi loved John and when he went anywhere he beckoned to John to be with him. Toward Peter his attitude was that of a father with a son whose nature was not yet formed and who was often bewildered by things which would become understandable to him when he had matured. But toward John, the attitude of the rabbi was that of a friend or a beloved brother. The others felt this unspoken closeness between the two of them, and, far from being jealous, it made them love the rabbi more.

The rabbi seemed always gentle and patient while John was impatient and far from gentle, for he had a very quick temper and a candor which was almost unnatural in a Jew. The rabbi had a sense of humor which was exquisite in its delicacy and never hurtful, but John had no sense of humor at all, and if he could not persuade others to see things his way by argument, then he called them fools to their face and was quite prepared, when thwarted, to use his fists.

While the rabbi seemed to be protecting Peter, waiting for him to reach that stature at which he could protect himself, John seemed to be protecting the rabbi. So when the rabbi announced that he would go to the wilderness to fast and pray John said that though it might not be necessary for Peter to accompany him, he, John, should be allowed to go along.

"There are many brigands, Rabbi," said John. "While I don't think they would beat you, for you are plainly poor, nonetheless they may mock you in which case I will wring their necks."

The rabbi laughed. "John," he said, "you would wrestle with Beelzebub himself."

"For you, Rabbi, indeed I would."

"Yet it is necessary with Beelzebub for each man to do his own wrestling," said the rabbi. "And so I go alone."

"Where and when will we find you, Rabbi?" asked John.

"As you found me before, so you will find me again," said the rabbi, and went.

With the rabbi gone, those who followed him were disconsolate and did not know what to do. Many people came to them to ask who the rabbi was—whether he was Elias or the Messiah; of the Pharisees or of the Sadducees or a follower of John the Baptizer or of Hillel, or one of the Hasidim or the Essenes or the Kiarites or of any of the dozen or more sects into which the Jewish religion was split without, however, being divided for all worshiped in the Temple. John answered these questions without hesitation, saying that the rabbi was the Messiah and that when he was ready he would bring the kingdom of God upon earth and raise an army, if he wished, out of the stones of Israel to overthrow the Romans and the incestuous and traitorous Herods.

Some believed him and others mocked him and said no man could turn stones into men and how did he think the rabbi could do such a thing. John replied, "You don't know the rabbi and I do know him, so how is it that you can tell me what the rabbi can do and what he cannot do, but you will not believe me who know him? You are fools. Why do you waste your time to come here to ask me questions when you have made up your minds not to believe my answers?"

"We would believe your answers if they were acceptable to our reason," they replied.

"Your reason?" said John. "Why, some of you have not got enough reason to keep yourselves out of debt and yet you would submit the rabbi to your reason. Tell me, can you put a bushel of olives into a one-pint measure?"

"No," they said.

"Well, then, neither can you get the rabbi into the measure of your minds. Who among you believes that Elias never died but was taken alive into Heaven?"

"We all so believe," they replied.

"So much for your reason," said John. "So be off with you and do good to one another and help the sick and the poor and patiently await the Kingdom of Heaven which the Messiah will bring to you."

John's statement that the rabbi from Nazareth was the Messiah had soon spread through the country and caused a great deal of concern among the doctors of the law, particularly in Jerusalem where the high priest had had enough of Messiahs and other self-appointed leaders. They feared that the Romans would suspect a plot and feared for their own authority over the people. They decided then that they would keep a close watch on the rabbi and keep the Roman authorities informed of any statements he made that could be interrupted as subversive. In this way they could best disassociate themselves from the rabbi. Not all, however, were of this opinion. Some, both of the Pharisees and of the Sadducees, of the greater and lesser councils of the Temple, kept an open mind on the rabbi, for they knew that their Father had not deserted his people and would one day send a Savior to them as he had promised.

It angered John that within a few days of the rabbi's departure some of the people began to disbelieve in his miracles. They said the huge catch of fish was some kind of phenomenon but nothing over which the rabbi had any control, and as for Veronica, she had probably not had leprosy at all but had been suffering from lack of food and exposure from which she had now recovered under the ministering of Susanna with whom she now lived.

John, as he grew angrier at these scoffings, became more outspoken and finally found himself summoned before the centurion at Capernaum to explain his statements about the rabbi. John was one of the Galileans who would not step aside in the road for a Roman or for a cohort of Romans, all armed, and he was not intimidated by the centurion but contemptuous of him.

"What is it to you, Roman, who the rabbi is?" he asked. "He has not come to you but to us, the children of Israel. He is ours. He would not lift his hand for you, a Gentile."

The soldier, Balba, who was present, and a little drunk as usual, struck John for his insolence but the centurion rebuked him. "Balba, you know the rule," he said. "No punishment without first of all judgment. This man has done no wrong."

"He's insolent," said Balba.

"He is not subject to discipline, as are you, and may not be struck," said Longinus. "Tell me, Jew, I hear that your rabbi is kin to John the Baptizer? Is that so?"

But John would not answer and Peter, who had gone with John, said, "Sir. We know little of our rabbi except that he is a holy man and loves the poor. We hear he is from Nazareth but we have not spoken to his parents about him. He has told us nothing of himself."

"What has he told you about anything?" asked Longinus.

"He has told us to pray and to do good works, which he says are the best of prayers, and to love the Father."

"And who is the Father?" asked the centurion.

"Why," said Peter, surprised, "who but God?"

"He does not say that he is himself the Father?" asked the centurion.

"That would be to blaspheme," said Peter, horrified.

"What does he say of his own relationship to the Father?"

"He says only what we all say—that he is the son of the Father, as are all the children of Israel."

"I heard that there is among you a society which is known as The Sons of the Father and that John the Baptizer and the robber Barabbas are among the leaders," said the centurion. "Is your rabbi a part of this?"

It was John who answered and hotly. "Neither our rabbi nor John the Baptizer would associate with such a man as Barabbas for he is anathema to us. He is unclean and an outcast and has the blood of innocents on his hands."

"See to it," said Longinus, "that you are not being led into some plot whose nature you will not know until you are already incriminated. Guard yourselves against folly. And you"—turning to John—"keep your mouth shut about a Messiah or you will be in trouble with your own priests before you are in trouble with me." Then he dismissed them.

When they were gone Balba said, "You should have put them away. That John is a hothead and will make enough trouble to tie up a legion before he is through."

"It isn't hotheads who bother me," said Longinus. "It is the quiet ones who say nothing and work secretly that I have to watch for." He remembered something and grinned at Balba and said, "I should send you to follow that rabbi. He is just the kind of miracle worker you would like."

"How so?" said Balba.

"At Cana, up in the hills, he turned water into wine," said the centurion.

"You're joking."

"That is what my informants say. And there were plenty who saw it."

Balba went to the door and looked after the two disciples of the rabbi, wondering.

* * * * * * * * * * *

The night after this episode Peter hardly slept. He was concerned at the suspicions of the centurion about the rabbi and at John's bold assertion that the rabbi was the Messiah, which the rabbi himself had never claimed to be. He was troubled too about his own lack of any real knowledge of the rabbi, and so he told John that he was going to find the rabbi's parents in Nazareth and ask them about their son.

He was aware of the stories that had drifted down from Nazareth concerning the rabbi's birth to a virgin, so that his father was in reality his foster father. But there were rumors that he had been conceived out of wedlock and the man Joseph had married the woman to save her shame, then the story put about that she had conceived through the spirit of God and not from man.

He had heard that the rabbi had been driven out of the synagogue at Nazareth for blasphemy, though he could not believe this was true and concluded that it was a lie told by the rabbi's detractors. So all in all it seemed best to go to Nazareth and find out what he could of the truth for himself.

John decided that he would accompany him, and Peter readily agreed to do this for he would be able to prevent John from making further rash statements about the rabbi in his absence. James and Andrew remained at Capernaum, and Andrew, mild and somewhat simple, said that until the rabbi returned they should start fishing again.

"Why?" demanded John. "Better to preach to the people about the rabbi. When we need fish, the rabbi will provide them. To fish, then, is a waste of time."

"I still think we should fish," said Andrew. "It is our proper work. I don't think we should ask the rabbi to do for us what we can do for ourselves."

"Do what you want," said John. "As for myself, I will never fish again."

By road the journey from Bethsaida to Nazareth was close to fifty miles and therefore took three days. The road followed the valley by the Sea of Galilee for fifteen miles and then struck a sturdy narrow track, unpaved, into the highlands capped by the lonely peak of Mount Tabor, which at this time of the year still had traces of snow, like a cloud smear, over its grim sides. The mountain was not high, but its isolation gave it the appearance of height, and as the two fishermen left the Jordan Valley to enter the highlands, they began to feel the air get colder, and the winds were from the west and blustering.

Several times they were caught in deluges of pelting rain and sleet and had to shelter in caves or under little cliffs. The air was chilled enough for their breath to form a vapor and they met few travelers, for this was the worst season to be going into the Galilee highlands. At times, following storms of rain, the road on which they traveled was turned briefly into a river of cold muddy water and the sound of water leaping down the hills was all around them drowning out even the whistle and howl of the wind. This thunder and roar of the water was hard on their nerves, particularly when, at nighttime, they felt the ground shake under them when a rock slide broke loose nearby.

Early on the second morning in the highlands, after a night of bellowing wind and hissing rain, the weather abated and they left the cave in which they had sheltered, hoping to reach Nazareth by nightfall. They had been on their way no more than half an hour when Peter, looking about at the spurs and ravines of mountain that came down to the road on either side, shouted, "Rabbi! Rabbi!" and, leaving the road, started to run up the mountainside.

John saw a figure a little way above them which he recognized immediately and set off after Peter, rejoicing in the thought that their sufferings were now at an end, for the rabbi, as soon as he saw how much they had suffered from wind and rain, would end the intemperance of the weather.

They had to cross a large ridge and descend a little draw to get to where the rabbi was, but when they neared the spot, he had disappeared. There was a cave in the flank of the mountain nearby and Peter, with John behind him, ran in there, sure that the rabbi was inside. The cave had a narrow entrance, forcing them to stoop to get inside, and indeed crawl for a few feet. But then it opened up into a large dry area which was lit by torches, and there was the rabbi, but surrounded by men armed with swords and knives. These men seized Peter and John as soon as they had struggled through the narrow entrance to the cave and Peter cried, "Rabbi, what have they done to you? Have they taken you prisoner?"

"Are you mad?" asked the man. "Who do you think I am?" The two looked at him in shock. He resembled the rabbi very closely and yet, now they could see him plainly, they realized they were mistaken.

"Sir," said Peter, "we do not know who you are and do not wish to know. Let us go on our way and we will say nothing of this."

"Tell me about your rabbi," said the man, and Peter did so.

When he had concluded, the man thought for a long time and then said, "You are both either out of your wits or have met one of the holy men of Israel. What is the name of this rabbi?"

"Jesus," said John.

"Go then and tell your rabbi I set you free," said the man. "Perhaps it will be remembered in my favor."

"What name shall we tell him?" asked Peter.

"Tell him Barabbas," said the man.

CHAPTER FOURTEEN

The village of Nazareth lay a little to the west of Mount Tabor and north of the Plain of Esdraelon, which separates the mountains of Galilee from those of Samaria. The plain was fertile but, lying between two massifs, received the water from both mountain ranges so that there were large bogs and marshes on the plain, through which it was impossible to pass.

Herod had many times spoken of draining these areas but, like his father, he preferred building palaces and amphitheaters and even cities to mere agricultural improvement and so no drainage plan had been drawn up. Herod was in love with the Greeks and would raise a thousand graceful columns in the Doric style before he put in one drainage ditch. The Plain of Esdraelon then, which could have matched the valley of the Jordan as a garden of Israel, was a wild place subject to devastating winter floods.

Nazareth lay on the shelf of one of the ridges which formed the foothills of Mount Tabor, the ridge itself ending in a precipice of a hundred feet. It was an ancient though small community and had been put in this location as a defense against invaders from Samaria to the south.

The people were almost all shepherds and the fleece of the sheep of Nazareth was highly valued, for the wildness of the climate produced a heavy crop of wool. Also prized was the honey of Nazareth, which had a particularly rich flavor because the bees visited the wild flowers of the mountains and so produced a dark sweet honey much superior to the bland rose honey of the warm Jordan Valley.

Neither Peter nor John had ever visited this mountain area and felt themselves among strangers and even foreigners though all were Jews. They were a short people, fair-skinned, blond-haired and some of them even red-haired. Though they spoke Aramaic it was with a clipped accent as if they begrudged every word and syllable, and they wore garments of homespun wool and some of them wore sheepskins flung over their shoulders as a protection against wind and rain.

They cut these sheepskins into a rough cape, with a hood that came over their heads, and wore their other garments at knee length, leaving their legs bare, and had no sandals on their feet. It was rare to see a man or a boy without a crook for catching sheep by the leg. All carried a leather wallet in which to keep their food, for they were often away from their homes for days with their flocks, and most carried slings since the men of this region were very skilled with this hunting weapon.

The two fishermen inquired for the home of the rabbi at the synagogue at Nazareth but got only black looks and found the house only by asking at the Roman military post, manned by three soldiers, which stood on the outskirts of the town. It was shameful to have to inquire there, but others whom they asked would give them no information, and one man told them to leave the town and not start stirring up the people.

"He is no rabbi but a blasphemer," said this man. "And with his blasphemy he has brought shame on his mother and on his brothers."

"What blasphemy has he said?" asked John.

"He has not spoken of it to you?" asked the man. "Well. He has good reason for his silence. One Sabbath he was asked to read from the Torah at the appointed place, but instead chose another which was not the scripture for the day. He read from Isaiah as follows: 'The Spirit of the Lord is upon me because he has anointed me; to bring good news to the poor he has sent me, to proclaim to the captives release, and sight to the blind; to set at liberty the oppressed, to proclaim the acceptable year of the Lord, and the day of recompense.' "

"He read then of the Messiah," said John.

"He read of the Messiah," said the man, "and then when he had finished reading he said, 'Today has this scripture been fulfilled in your hearing.' And for this blasphemy, claiming to be the Messiah when we know he is only the son of a builder, he was seized and dragged from the synagogue to the precipice and would have been thrown over to his death. But he escaped."

"Were there many of them that laid hands on him?" asked John.

"The whole of the people," said the man.

"Then why could they not throw him to his death?"

"That I cannot say," said the man. "We were about to hurl him over and then we were afraid and let him go. He walked through us and no one laid a hand on him."

"Because he is indeed the Messiah," said John. "And you dared to lay hands on him, you accursed narrow men who speak grudgingly to strangers and will not direct the traveler on his way."

"Peace," said Peter. "Peace. I beg of you."

"Bah," said John. "I doubt I will leave this place without knocking some heads together." He turned from the man without the traditional phrases of farewell and it was then they inquired the way of the soldiers and found the house of Joseph, the builder, now dead, and his wife, Mary.

The woman was alone in the house, which was very small and on the outskirts of the village and approached by a narrow and muddy lane. The house had but one room, and at one end of this room there was a bench with a wood vice and saws, chisels and mallets in a rack on the wall.

It was dark when they got to the house and they made enough noise, stumbling up the lane, for the woman, Mary, to be aware of their approach, and as they reached the door, she opened it, holding an oil lamp in her hand. She shielded the flame against the wind so that the light was reflected on her face and when John saw that face, calm, patient, yet expressive of a deep sorrow, he fell to his knees before her and exclaimed, "Hail Mary, full of grace. The Lord is with thee. Blessed are thou amongst women and blessed is the fruit of thy womb: Jesus."

"How do you know these words?" she said, the lamp trembling in her hand.

"Mother," said John, "they came from my heart but I do not know how they came."

"Surely then you have come from God," she said, and let them in. She seemed afraid of them and trembled as she started to prepare food. Turning from the fire at last she said, "If you be angels, then tell me for I am afraid lest I offended against the Lord in letting my son go from here though he told me that his time had come."

"How can we be angels?" asked Peter. "We are but fishermen from Galilee."

"And yet this one spoke the words of an angel which were spoken to me before my son was conceived and which I have kept hidden in my heart from everyone except my spouse Joseph." Then she told them how she had been visited by the Angel Gabriel when she was betrothed to Joseph, but many months before their marriage, and the angel had told her she would conceive a son whom she would call Jesus and that God would give him the throne of David and he would be king over the House of Jacob forever and of his kingdom there would be no end.

"And I said to the angel, 'How shall this be for, although I am betrothed, yet I am a virgin and do not know man and shall not know man for many months for the day of my wedding is far off.' Then the angel said to me, 'The Holy Spirit shall come upon thee and the power of the Most High shall overshadow thee; and therefore the Holy One to be born shall be called the son of God.' And to this I replied, though fearful, 'Behold the handmaiden of the Lord; be it done to me according to thy word.' And the child was born as the angel had foretold and was named Jesus."

"And he was not the child of your husband?" asked Peter.

"I knew not my husband as man in all the years of my marriage," said Mary. "Those whom they call the brothers of Jesus are his cousins for in this part it is the custom to say of cousins that they are brothers. I am a virgin to this day and what lay between me and my husband was not of the flesh but of the love of the spirit only which abides for all time."

"And was the child born here in Nazareth?" asked Peter.

"No," said Mary. "In Bethlehem, in the time of Augustus when the census was taken. For we are of the House of David and following the decree had to journey to Bethlehem to register there."

"In Bethlehem," said Peter, looking at John, and they both knew the significance of that statement, for all Jews had learned from scripture that from Bethlehem would come the Savior.

"He is then the Holy One of God," said John, "and even if you had not told us these things, we would have known because of the wonders he has worked in our presence." He then told Mary of the miraculous catch of fish and the curing of the leper woman and asked whether the rabbi had worked any wonders in Nazareth.

She shook her head. "Here, where all know him as the son of the builder, none believe him and indeed they revile him," she said. "It is hard for them to believe for they have known him since his birth almost thirty years. They have seen him struggling as they also struggle with his work. They worked beside him when a new roof was to be put on the synagogue which took three months, for the timbers were heavy and had to be brought here from afar. His tools became as blunt as theirs; he became as weary as they; he failed as many times as they did. They could not believe that he is anything but another man like themselves. And indeed, the wonders he works are always based on faith and before he performs any miracle he first tests the faith of those who ask it. If the faith is firm and unquestioning, he performs the miracle. But if the faith is lacking, he will do nothing.

"In our talks here in this house in the evenings when my husband Joseph, who was a good man, was still alive, it was not Joseph who educated my son in God but my son who educated Joseph. And the one lesson he stressed was that for salvation faith in the goodness of God was the first essential and nothing could be done without it."

"I wonder then," said Peter, "that he should have called me. For my own faith is imperfect and I have many times ignored the Law and lived sinfully."

"Peter," said Mary, "did you not all your life desire to believe?"

"With all my heart," said Peter with great earnestness.

"For this reason you were called," said Mary. "For my son said many times, 'Seek and you shall find. Knock and it shall be opened to you.' "

"Then my mind is at peace," said Peter. But he was immediately seized with uncertainty and said, "Yet, what has happened in the past will happen again for I am a man given to weakness."

"As for me," said John, "I have no doubts. I know the rabbi to be the Messiah. I will follow him to death."

"John," said Mary. "You too have your weakness."

"How can that be?" asked John. "I believe. No man will shake me."

"What do you think of my son—that he will be like Caesar and conquer the world?"

"There is no doubt about it," said John. "When the rabbi wills it, the day of deliverance will come. The Gentiles will be smitten and dismayed and God will fulfill his promise of deliverance to his people. And I will be at the rabbi's side, that day, with my brother James, and the only argument between us will be who shall cut off the head of Herod Antipas."

"John, John," said Mary. "Your faith blinds you, and you do not know the mission of the rabbi. Listen to him, not with your mind made up as to what his mission is, but to discover the real reason of his being. For God has not sent his son into the world to fulfill the ambitions of men, but to do the bidding of the Father."

"But he has promised us a deliverer," said John.

"Think from what we are to be delivered," said Mary. "Whether it is from the rule of the Gentiles or from the fetters we have placed about ourselves." John was disturbed and confused by these words, but out of respect for the mother of the rabbi did not pursue the matter further.

They stayed with the rabbi's mother for a week and on the Sabbath went with her to the synagogue, where she was seated in the court with the women while they, as men, were admitted to the main part of the synagogue but were seated in the back of the place. It was the custom when a stranger visited the synagogue for him to be called to read from the appointed place in the Torah. The elders then beckoned to John to enter the pulpit and put the opened roll before him. They were angry when he came at their first bidding for it was the custom to refuse three times to read as being unworthy.

The verse which was to be read was from Isaiah and went as follows: "For Sion's sake I will not hold my peace, and for the sake of Jerusalem I will not rest till her Just One come forth as brightness, and her Savior be lighted as a lamp. And the Gentiles shall see thy Just One and all kings thy Glorious One, and thou shall be called by a new name, which the mouth of the Lord shall name."

When he had finished the reading John left the lectern and returned to his place. They asked him then to comment on the scripture and John returned to the pulpit and said, "Who, if he does not believe the Just One, can be expected to believe the disciple of the Just One? For the Just One you have had among you and you threw him from this place, calling him the son of Joseph the builder."

That was as far as he got. The congregation was on its feet in a moment hissing and shouting him down, but John's anger was greater than theirs and taking up the roll of the scripture in his hand he defied them to touch him. Thinking him a madman who, if he was further angered would desecrate the scripture, they did not touch him and John said to them, "You think I blaspheme and would tear me apart. If I did indeed blaspheme do you not believe that God would strike me down? Or do you think yourselves greater than God—that he is powerless and so you must be his avengers?

"You hypocrites who have taken to yourselves the place of God! Of what avail is your fasting and your purification and your offerings at the Temple if you cast God out from among yourselves?"

The rabbi turned to the congregation and said, "He blasphemes. You have heard the blasphemy yourselves. He whom he calls the Holy One is the son of the builder and we know that, all of us . . ."

"You are blind," cried John, cutting him off, "and so cannot see. And deaf and so cannot hear. But listen to me, those who are not deaf, and I will tell you of him."

He then related the story of the fish and the curing of

the leper woman but was met with shouts of derision. "These wonders you relate he worked in Capernaum but he was thirty years among us and worked no wonders, but sweated like any other man at his daily toil," the rabbi said.

"He worked no wonders among you because you would not believe," said John. "If there was one among you that believed, then he would for that one perform a miracle." The furore in the main body of the synagogue had been watched in fearful silence by the women, separated from the men by a grill. Then a woman's voice was raised from that section.

The woman said, "I have with me my daughter who when she is touched is bruised, and when she is cut even with a thorn bleeds and the bleeding will not stop. If he of whom you speak is the Holy Onc, and you his disciple, cannot you then cure my child?"

"Let her place her hand through the grill," said John.

"Sir," said the woman, "the opening is small—her hand will be bruised and cut and the bleeding will not stop. Yet I will do as you say."

The girl's hand was small and the skin pale. But small as it was, it had to be forced through the opening in the grill so that the skin was cut and blood flowed from it. John descended from the pulpit and the congregation, mocking, let him pass but crowded around, and he knew that if he failed they would tear him apart as a blasphemer. John then put his hand on that of the girl's and said aloud, "Father, not for my glory, but for love of my rabbi, your son, I pray that you cure this child who has shown her faith in you."

Immediately the bleeding stopped. Indeed the blood

itself vanished and when the child withdrew her hand from the grill, though it was scraped in so doing, it showed neither a cut nor a bruise.

Some of them in the congregation believed, particularly among the women. But the men said that the child had been recovering from her sickness for some time and others said that the sickness was only a fancy of the mother's who was overprotective of her daughter and thought every cut or bruise a grievous wound.

Peter was shocked and angry at John's audacity. "You might have failed and shamed the rabbi," he said.

"Failed?" cried John. "How could I fail? Did I not call on God in the name of our rabbi who is the Messiah? It was not possible for me to fail."

Peter wondered at this and prayed from that day that his own faith might be stronger and his nature less inclined to wavering and doubts.

CHAPTER FIFTEEN

Pontius Pilate, procurator of Judaea, had at this time achieved a minor wonder by remaining in office for five years as the immediate governor of a people less amenable to rule than even the German tribes of the Danube frontier. In part, the length of his tenure was the result of his own astuteness, including his ability to listen carefully to the counsel of others while never revealing his own mind. In part also it was the result of the acquiescence of the leaders of the Jews who had learned that it was better for one plunderer to remain a long time in office than to have a succession of short-term plunderers, voracious as horseflies, descend on them.

For a year after he had taken office the Jews had kept careful watch on him through an espionage system that penetrated Pilate's own household and of which Pilate himself knew. He would have refused to believe that such an espionage system did not operate against him, and he himself had its counterpart in the Temple, in all the towns of Judaea, and indeed in the Tetrarchies of both Herod Philip and Herod Antipas. For a year then there had been a joint feeling out of power and of disposition on the part of the interior government of the Jews led by the High Priest Annas and on the part of Pilate representing Rome.

And then Pilate, who well knew the efficacy of the maxim "Divide and Rule," applied that principle in Judaea. He did it at a time when a certain friendliness was developing on the part of the High Priest Annas—a friendliness which had even gone to the extent of the private entertainment of Pilate in the house of the high priest, though it would better be called a palace for Pilate had rarely seen such richness of building, of furniture and gardens. Pilate replied to this gesture of friendliness by appointing a second high priest—Caiphas—at one stroke thereby demonstrating the authority of Rome and his indifference to the friendship and influence of Annas and also splitting the allegiance of the Jews between two high priests.

Pilate handled the matter cunningly. When a delegation led by Annas called on him to protest the appointment, he held the hearing publicly on the terrace of his palace at Caesarea and blandly insisted that the action was taken to prevent a tumult among the people, and that he himself was indifferent to who was high priest for the religion of the Jews was of no concern to him.

"There can be only one high priest," Annas stated. "The election must be made from the Sanhedrin from four families who have traditionally filled the office. The matter is one only of our religion. The duties of the high priest are concerned only with the Temple and Rome has promised to honor and protect our religion from the time of Pompey. Each emperor since then has pledged that this shall be done."

"It is to protect your religion that I have appointed Caiphas as co-high priest," said Pilate. "Many question your election. That does not benefit your religion. This has been done for the good of yourself and your god."

"It is only the Galileans who have stirred up trouble," said Annas. "They have always been stiff-necked and rebellious."

"Ah yes, only the Galileans," said Pilate. "Now how many did we have to kill to put down that last riot in the Temple? A score or more, I believe. Slain right before the altar of sacrifice and a few priests among them. And why, my friend? Was it not because they questioned some regulations you had made concerning their sacrifices and called you a usurper and a profaner of the Temple?

"I agree that these religious matters are not my concern. But when they are felt so severely as to cause a riot in the Temple, daily crowded with thousands of others, then I must exert the authority of Rome to maintain the peace. The solution is excellent. You are the high priest for those of Judaea who are devoted to you. Caiphas is the high priest for the Galileans. You may alternate your duties."

"But there can be only one high priest," Annas insisted. "There can be only one in the whole nation who, having purified himself in body and in mind, dares to enter the Holy of Holies on the Day of Atonement and pronounce the forbidden name of God."

"And what would happen if another, not the high priest, did this?" asked Pilate.

"He would assuredly be reduced to ashes," said Annas.

"Then let us see how Caiphas fares when he enters the Holy of Holies," said Pilate. "If he is reduced to ashes as being a false high priest, the problem is solved. If he is not, and you are not, it would seem that your God has no objection to two high priests."

He then dismissed Annas and when, on the following Day of Atonement, both high priests entered the Holy of

Holies in succession and neither was immolated, Pilate had gained his objective, and divided the Jews even in their religion, for there was no longer one all-powerful high priest in Israel to lead them.

He had also gained a minor victory over his wife Procula, who was highly superstitious and had pleaded with him, under the influence of her Jewish advisers, to cancel the appointment of Caiphas, who was actually the son-in-law of Annas. The superstitions of his wife, surrounded by fortune tellers, astrologers, numerologists, soothsayers, interpreters of dreams and diviners of every kind—diviners of stones, of water, of trees, of birds, of wind and of clouds—was one of the obstacles to his government of Judaea which Pilate had to combat and overcome.

Those who knew Pilate best, and there were few who knew him really well, suspected that division was not, however, the sole object of his appointment of a second high priest. They were right, for shortly afterward Pilate sent a cohort, under the senior centurion at Jerusalem, to seize the treasury of the Temple, which he knew to be worth a tremendous fortune, the money to be used to build an aqueduct to supply Caesarea with water.

This caused a riot in the city in which two hundred were killed and had repercussions in Rome, for the matter was reported directly to Rome by Annas, who sent a delegation to Tiberius to protest the seizure of the sacred funds. But the riot was not as great as might have been expected, for Annas' denouncing the seizure was not joined as heartily by Caiphas or by the supporters of Caiphas. Furthermore, Pilate, whose immediate superior was Lucius Vitellus, governor of Syria, had discussed the venture with Vitellus and put such an interpretation on the plan as to make the building of the acqueduct a matter of the security of Rome in Judaea.

His arguments were simple. The Jews were subjected to a double taxation—that of Rome and that of their Temple. The Temple taxation, imposed as a religious duty, was paid first and in full and left less money available for Roman taxation. From Roman taxes, hardly enough was obtained, said Pilate, to support the Roman government and its legions in Judaea, and there was very little left over for the coffers of the emperor.

"The Temple drains off money which should be available to us," said Pilate. "The Temple taxes, imposed under the guise of religious devotion, are actually a subtle weapon used against Rome, drying up the source of our revenue. If we increase our taxes, there is riot against Roman rule. At the level at which we are obliged to keep the taxes, little money can be spent on strengthening our military position in Judaea. Caesarea, which as you know is only one port on this coast, lacks water. In a siege the garrison would soon be reduced by thirst. But an aqueduct bringing water from the hills would strengthen the position of Caesarea, which must be held if Judaea itself is to be held. Therefore I plan to seize the Temple treasury to build such an aqueduct."

Vitellus was too wise a ruler either to approve or forbid the plan. If he forbade it, he would be in the position of neglecting to strengthen Caesarea. If he approved it, he would be involved in the tumult the action would arouse in Judaea and in Rome at the court of Tiberius. He merely warned Pilate of the likely results and the cohort marched into the Temple and seized the treasure, which was deposited in the Antonia fortress.

Pilate was careful to remain in Caesarea when this took

place. He refused for three weeks to see the delegation sent to protest, and when he at last saw the delegates and they accused him of taking money that belonged to their god, he replied that he had been informed that the god of the Jews was not interested in riches of the world but only in the good character of men. He was warned that Jerusalem was in a turmoil over the seizure and even the pleadings of the priests, who had tried to calm the population, could not prevent rioting which would continue until the treasure was returned.

"I will go myself to Jerusalem," said Pilate.

"Excellency," said the High Priest Annas, "that would not be wise. We cannot guarantee the temper of the people. Your life may be endangered."

"I do not ask you to guarantee the temper of the people who are the subjects of Rome," replied Pilate grimly. "I will control that myself."

He went to Jerusalem with a military escort and was hissed at by the mob. But he had laid his plans carefully. A thousand of his soldiers, dressed as civilians, were collected near the Temple and armed with cudgels. These charged the Jews who hissed at Pilate, battering them to the ground, and Pilate ordered his cavalry to put down the riot. Those who fell under the cudgels were trampled to death by the horses. Others were crushed to death in the panic. Horsemen chased those who fled down the narrow streets, trampling them under or impaling them with their spears against the walls of houses. There was no count of the dead or injured, but two days were needed to clear the area around the Temple of blood and bodies.

Then Pilate returned a small portion of the treasure to the Temple, exacting a receipt for a greater amount. He had some money for the aqueduct and, it was said, a larger amount for himself. He sent a letter to Vitellus regretting the bloodshed but pointing out that the riot had been caused by the Jews themselves, some of whom, armed with cudgels, had attacked those who hissed at him and, in doing so, insulted Rome.

Vitellus, who knew the details, congratulated Pilate on upholding the Roman authority but was wise enough to return a present of money which Pilate sent him.

Pilate had by this time come to his own conclusion concerning the Jews and their religion. The religion of the Jews, he believed, was a conspiracy evolved through the centuries for preserving the Jewish people and spreading their dominance throughout the known world. It was a conspiracy aimed at world conquest, and in this aim it was succeeding to a remarkable degree for there were Jewish communities in every city of the empire and these communities wielded an influence out of all proportion to their numbers. To the Roman maxim "Divide and Rule" the Jews supplied the answer, "Unite and Conquer." Unity was achieved by proclaiming that there was but one god and that this god had made the Jews his chosen people. Outwardly Judaea was subject to Rome. But in fact the people of Judaea and all Jews throughout the empire were governed from the Temple in Jerusalem, through the High Priest and the Sanhedrin, which was a kind of senate of the Jewish government. Rome was bound to protect the religion of the Jews, through the compact with Pompey honored by his successors. But when the compact was made Rome had not realized that the religion they protected was a conspiracy aimed at Jewish world dominance.

It was when he had made up his mind in this manner that Pilate evolved his policy toward the Jews. The policy was aimed at the destruction of their religion while pretending to protect it, or making only such open moves against it as could be defended as being in the interests of Rome.

A first step had been the appointment of a rival high priest to Annas. A second step was the reduction of the Jewish war chest by appropriating the treasure in the Temple. A third step was the promotion of a Greek influence among them, though this policy had been inaugurated by Herod the Great with such success that the whole of Palestine was now as much Greek as Jewish. A fourth step called for a modulation of a policy set when he first took office as procurator.

At that time he had decided to support the high priest, arguing that the Temple could become a tool of Roman power. But he later decided that it would be better to support the various prophets, seers, miracle workers and saviors who appeared from time to time among the people and were inimical to the Pharisees whom he held formed the political party behind the anti-Roman Temple conspiracy.

Unfortunately for him few of these rebel leaders appeared in his own province of Judaea proper and Samaria to the north. Most appeared in the Tetrarchy of Herod Antipas, where the authority of the Pharisees was not so strong. There was John the Baptizer in Peraea and now news from Longinus at Capernaum of another, Jesus of Nazareth, a miracle worker and significantly a cousin of John's.

The Capernaum centurion had reported several miracles worked by Jesus which Pilate skipped, for these things, the common appendages of all saviors, no longer impressed him. He was interested, however, in the Capernaum centurion's statement that this Jesus, the cousin of John the Baptizer, had gone into the wilderness of Peraea, presumably for a meeting with John.

"I have questioned two followers of the Rabbi Jesus, John son of Zebedee and Peter son of Jonah, both at Capernaum, and they have denied that the rabbi is part of the conspiracy of The Sons of the Father," the centurion reported. "I have known these two men for ten years. They are fishermen and not of the kind that lend themselves to conspiracy. They stress that neither John the Baptizer nor the Rabbi Jesus would associate with Barabbas, who is unclean in that he has robbed and murdered which is contrary to the strict commandments of the Jews. It is my experience that such a man as Barabbas could not lead a conspiracy or revolt among the Jews. Nonetheless I have warned the fishermen John and Peter not to be led innocently into subversion. I have not questioned or observed Jesus of Nazareth myself, for he left this area for the Peraea wilderness shortly after my return from Caesarea. I have had only one contact with him, in the following circumstances." The report then related the catch of fish which was attributed by all as a miracle of the rabbi's.

"The fisherman John has several times stated that Jesus is the Messiah or Savior of these people, but Peter will not go so far. I have heard that the Baptizer has referred to Jesus as the Messiah, and the Rabbi Jesus himself has said he is the deliverer spoken of by the Jewish prophet, Isaiah. But he has not spoken against the government of Rome and I have found no grounds to arrest him."

When he had considered this report Pilate sent a letter to Longinus instructing him not to interfere with the rabbi, but to protect him against any violence. The rabbi, he decided, could be used as a weapon for shaking the allegiance of the Jews to their high priests and the Pharisees. So also could John the Baptizer with whom the rabbi was plainly linked. Pilate was not quite ready to dismiss Barabbas as part of the conspiracy. He knew no scruples himself and could not believe that they really existed in others. Barabbas, he still suspected, was probably forming the nucleus of the military army of the conspiracy to which he had given the name "The Sons of the Father." John was a propagandist and probably expendable, and the rabbi of Nazareth was likely the true leader because he was the one who was working the wonders.

The conspiracy, when developed, would of course be dangerous to Rome and at that time would have to be suppressed and the leaders executed. But until it was fully developed it could be subtly encouraged, for it would serve the purpose of alienating some of the Jews from the high priests and the Temple.

Pilate therefore secretly ordered Longinus at Capernaum to take no steps against the rabbi of Nazareth, nor John nor even Barabbas until he had express orders to do so from the procurator himself.

"Let me know more about this rabbi," Pilate concluded. "Secure a list of his followers. Report on the places he visits, the people he sees, the things he preaches. But do not move against him. Rather, encourage him."

CHAPTER SIXTEEN

The fame of John the Baptizer had soon spread through the whole of the land and into Syria and Phoenicia and Cappadocia to the north and Arabia and Egypt and Libya to the south and west. Though he worked no wonders, curing none who were sick, his words and his presence themselves were wonder enough. He exactly fitted the Jewish concept and tradition of the prophets, and Jews and even Gentiles flocked to him in the mountainous deserts beyond the Jordan. They came in such numbers that their very passage through the desert made new roads over its barren and frightening hills, roads which were beaten out by the passage of camels, donkeys and hundreds of thousands of human feet.

John was a prophet and was contemptuous of the world's riches, goods and comforts, as were the prophets of old, and this appealed to all. He was a wild, solitary, uncompromising figure whose voice had the grandeur and directness of thunder. He threw aside the scruples of the Law and spoke without fear as had Elias and Jeremiah and Isaiah. The words he spoke were like theirs—scalding, lashing words of doom, demanding repentance before it was too late, and promising salvation for those who repented. That he came from the wilderness was deeply significant for the wilderness was to the Jews an overwhelming presence that surrounded and threatened and in places cut into their fertile valleys.

The lush purple figs they harvested, the plump and abundant olives, the golden rustling grain, all these they knew were temporary things. The wilderness itself was eternal and the same wilderness that Abraham their father had known. They feared the wilderness for the wrath of God lay there, and those who were from the wilderness knew the mind of God and what he demanded of his people. The words of the prophet froze his listeners with fear and brought them, with ashes already smeared into their hair, to his presence.

"Brood of vipers," he told them when they came. "Who has shown you how to flee from the wrath to come?

"The ax is laid to the root of the tree, and every tree that is not bringing forth fruit will be cut down and thrown into the fire.

"Tremble then before the ax of God. Pray not for mercy but deserve mercy by bringing forth good fruit for in this harvest only is your salvation. Tremble you who offer gifts of gold and of silver at the Temple but drive the beggar from the door as unworthy. Do you think to trick your God, you unclean of mind whose hearts are stones?

"Do not comfort yourselves by saying, 'We have Abraham for our father' for I say to you that God is able out of these stones to raise up children to Abraham. Bring forth fruits of repentance while there is yet time. The wheat will be gathered into the barn and the chaff will be burned with unquenchable fire." These were powerful words and had tremendous effect.

To those who asked the prophet, "What then shall we

do?" he replied. "Run not to the Temple with offerings to bribe your God. But let him who has two tunics share with him who has none; and let him who has food share with him who is hungry."

Some who were tax collectors and therefore despised by all Jews for serving Rome begged John to tell them how they could be saved, for they despaired of salvation. "Shall we leave our posts?" they asked. "If so others will be appointed in our place and the people of Israel will still groan under their taxes. Master, what must we do?"

"Exact no more than what has been appointed to you," the Baptizer replied. "Your hands are in the purses of the widow and the orphan. See that you extract only what is demanded by your masters, for if you take out one mite beyond that, you rob not the widow but yourself of your own salvation."

Among those who came to him were some of the soldiers of Herod, who were many of them Jews. These asked, "And we who are subject to orders which we cannot disobey except at the penalty of scourging or death—what are we to do?"

"You have the key to every man's house, and the entrance to every man's vineyard," replied John. "See then that you plunder none and accuse none falsely to justify your plundering. Be subject to your discipline and content with your pay but see that you do not make out of your position a scourge for your brothers."

Those who agreed to follow these teachings, among them many soldiers and tax collectors, merchants and money changers, John led into the river and immersed them completely in the water as a symbol that they were washed clean of their past life and all their misdeeds. But he knew the people well; knew their ability to confuse the outward act with the inward change and warned them that the immersion was but a sign which if not accompanied by a change of their hearts was without value.

Many asked him whether he was the Messiah and he was content for a while to tell them, with some anger, that he was not. But when this question became more often asked, and there was a crowd of several thousands listening to him, he silenced them and said in his thunderous voice, "You see that I baptize you with water. But one mightier than I is coming, the strap of whose sandals I am not worthy to loose. He will baptize you with the Holy Spirit and with fire, and that baptism will not be of water, which is but the symbol, but of the spirit of God himself.

"He of whom I speak has the winnowing fan in his hand, and he will clean out his threshing floor of all dust and dirt and he will gather the wheat into his barn and the chaff he will burn up with unquenchable fire."

The high priests, Annas and Caiphas, had by this time come to a compromise with each other, for they were both troubled about the effect on the people of the preaching of John. So they sent to question him a young rabbi named Saul, and they selected him because of his learning but also because he was a Roman and whatever report he brought back about John would be acceptable to both the Jews and the Romans.

Saul was one of the Hasidim, the extremists among the Pharisees, who held that every scruple of the Law, whether the written law or tradition, must be observed. He was a young man, and his youth gave him an enthusiasm for the Law and a rejection of compromise which won him the respect of the Pharisaic party and even fear, and he had it in common with John the Baptizer that he did not hesitate to attack even the highest in the land.

Equally Jew and Roman, he had two names—Saul, his Jewish name, and Gaius Julius Paulus, his Roman name taken from his father, who was a Roman citizen of the city of Tarsus in Cilicia. He was at the time in his mid-twenties and had studied in Jerusalem at the school of Gamaliel, the grandson of Hillel and the greatest of the rabbinical teachers of that time.

Such a man, patriotic Roman and devout Jew, was the ideal person to send to question the prophet John and see whether he could not be tripped into either blasphemy or error in his view of the Law, or sedition against the Roman governors. He came then before John as the champion of the Temple, his clothing correct in every detail even down to the length of the fringes on his robes, and for several days he listened to the preaching of the prophet but said nothing. His very silence became impressive and the multitudes increased, for they knew from rumor his errand and wanted to see how the prophet would answer the questions that would eventually be put to him by the learned young rabbi.

Then the day came that Saul questioned John, and the question he threw at him, quietly put, had the impact of a thunderbolt. "What say you to the marriage of Herod to Herodias, the wife of his brother?" he asked.

"Saul," said John, "I know you well. You are one of much learning, but of no wisdom. You know the last letter of the Law and nothing of its spirit. With the letter of the Law you have devised a scourge to chasten the people. But the spirit of the Law will provide a scourge for you within yourself that will lay the bones of your soul bare. You will be struck to the ground and brought down from your high place and in this scourging you will find your redemption."

"And Herod and Herodias?" said Saul softly. "Let us

concern ourselves with them. What have you to say to their marriage?"

"Answer me straight," said John. "Is Herod here or have you been sent by Herod?"

"He is not here and I am sent from the Temple."

"If you are sent from the Temple, what have those in the Temple to say of Herod's marriage?" asked John. "What has Annas to say and Caiphas? Are not these the appointed speakers for the people? Are not these the high priests and leaders? Why then do they keep a silence as if they were dumb? They are silent because they fear for themselves but have no fear for the Law which they twist to serve their own ends so that it is a tool in their hands. They will accept Herod and his wife Herodias but reject the little dove of the poor as unworthy if there is one feather which is not white as snow. Saul, what say you to that? Should the blemished dove be rejected with scorn, for which the widow has paid the last of her coins, but no word spoken by the high priests against Herod?"

To this Saul, discomforted, could make no answer.

"Saul, Saul," said John. "You have taken a wrong road and will not turn back until the precipice gapes before you. Return to those who sent you and tell them that that which I would say of Herod, I will say to Herod, that he may hear directly the words that God will put in my mouth concerning him. For God will not speak to Herod through your report to Annas and Caiphas, but in the words which I will say to Herod himself."

Saul then returned to Jerusalem to make his report to the high priests. He was much troubled for some of his own certainty in the Law had been shaken by the words of John the Baptizer; but, feeling his faith a little shaken, he strengthened his resolve against this temptation and steeled his will to abide all the more by the letter of the Law and permit no doubts concerning its exactness in all matters.

After Saul had gone, the rabbi from Nazareth appeared among the multitude that flocked to John. He came in the evening when John was baptizing a great number of people in the river, and there was a line of these waiting for the immersion. The rabbi took his place at the end of the line, but some who knew him from the wonders he had performed in Capernaum spoke to John and told him that the rabbi was in the crowd of those awaiting baptism.

John then sought him and kneeling said, "Rabbi, it is I rather who should be baptized by you. Why then do you come to me?"

But the rabbi said, "Let it be done that an example may be set to these others of the symbol of the rebirth which each man must undergo for his salvation."

John still demurred, but the rabbi said to him, "What I ask of you is the will of the Father and you shall have a sign from the Father that this is so."

John then led the rabbi into the river and put his hand on the rabbi's shoulder and submerged him below the water of the river. As he did so he said aloud, "This baptism I perform at the command of him who is baptized and in the name of the Father."

When the rabbi arose from the river the sun, which had been sinking below a purpling bank of clouds in the west, shone forth with the strength of midday, and a white dove was seen to flutter over his head. Then, some said from the sky and, others said, from the mountains of the wilderness, a voice was heard saying, "This is my beloved son, in whom I am well pleased."

Then John, who had received his sign, said, "My work is done, Lord. I go now to Herod."

The eyes of the rabbi filled with tears and he said for all around to hear, "What have you come here to see? A prophet? Yes, I tell you, and more than a prophet. This is he of whom it is written, 'Behold I send my messenger before thy face, who shall make ready thy way before thee. Amen I say to you, among those born of women there has not risen a greater than John the Baptist. . . .' "

And so they parted and John did not preach again except before Herod Antipas.

CHAPTER SEVENTEEN

When Peter and John returned from Nazareth they told James and Andrew and Judas of Kerioth all that the mother of the rabbi had related to them, and of the enmity against the rabbi in his own village. Judas alone was not shocked at this news. He had more knowledge of the world than the others. He said it was natural that the rabbi should be so treated in his birthplace. Envy itself would produce such a reaction and the rabbi would do well never again to visit Nazareth, where he would meet with nothing but indignity.

John was angry at Judas and asked him whether he would presume to give advice to the rabbi who was the Messiah. Judas said John was wrong to call the rabbi the Messiah when he himself had never made such a claim.

"In your lifetime and mine," he said, "there have been a score and more Messiahs in this land. Where are they now? They are all discredited or crucified. If you do not want our rabbi to suffer the same fate, you will do well not to call him the Messiah. We do not know who he is except that he is a holy man who loves the poor. He will tell us himself whether he is the Messiah."

"Bah," said John. "You have a head of hard stone.

You have to be told in so many words or else you will not believe. Are not the wonders he has performed sufficient proof without his spelling the thing out for you? He proclaims through his works who he is. It is not for him to say that he is the Messiah but for us to recognize that this is so. Does a king say 'I am the king' or do the people say 'He is the king'? So it will be with the Messiah. When the people have come to acknowledge him, as they will, then his kingdom will come and all the troubles of the whole world will be at an end."

To this Judas said nothing, for John was no man to oppose when he was angry, and he was easily angered. But Judas reflected deeply on the matter and reflected on the miracle John had performed in the synagogue at Nazareth in the name of the rabbi of which he had been told. James was openly pleased that his brother had performed this miracle and delighted in telling others about it in detail though he had not been there. Andrew, the brother of Peter, a mild and gentle man, accepted it as perfectly natural.

But Judas considered it a special grace which had come from the rabbi and which might one day be accorded to him if he was scrupulous in following the rabbi's teachings. This he resolved all the more to do and in the smallest detail. He yearned for the power to work a miracle which would offset the distrust people had of him as a man of business. Awaiting the return of the rabbi, then, he prayed constantly and fasted twice a week and avoided any act or occasion which might render him unclean. In this he differed from the others, who mixed freely with the people, ate with them and often took food which, bought from Gentiles, might be impure.

As the days went by and the rabbi had not returned,

Peter became more and more concerned about their reunion. He asked the others whether they should not go into the wilderness across the Sea of Galilee and look for him. John, remembering their misadventure with Barabbas (of which he had reported the details to Longinus the centurion at Capernaum), worried whether the rabbi had not fallen among some of the robber bands that hid out in the trans-Jordan wilderness.

With the passing of the days, inaction became intolerable. Four weeks went by and then five from the time of the rabbi's departure. A rumor reached them that the rabbi had been with John the Baptizer and then came a further and frightening rumor that John the Baptizer had been arrested by Herod and was now chained to the wall of the grim dungeon at Machaerus, awaiting Herod's pleasure.

This disturbed them all so much for the safety of the rabbi that Peter sought out Longinus to ask whether the news was true and whether the rabbi had incurred Herod's displeasure.

He learned that John the Baptizer was indeed Herod's prisoner, but the rabbi had not been arrested nor had any of John's disciples. Conscious of Pilate's instruction to offer some protection to the rabbi, Longinus treated Peter kindly and spoke to him alone about the rabbi so the fisherman could speak freely of him.

He was surprised and touched by the depth of the fisherman's devotion and love for the rabbi—some measure of which lay in the fact that Peter, a Jew, would come to him, a Roman, for news. The centurion himself began to feel some warmth toward the rabbi, and he told Peter that he would inquire from the various stations under his command whether the rabbi had been seen anywhere and would inform him if he had any news of him.

"God will bless you, Roman, if you do," said Peter. Peter had previously only looked at the centurion as a Roman officer—a figure in a uniform who represented a foreign and conquering power. Now he looked at Longinus closely as a man and saw the lined face and the grim jaw and the eyes of someone who seemed lost. He was surprised to see a suggestion of loneliness on a Roman face but did not dare to say anything.

Finally the waiting became too much for Peter and he reflected on the rabbi's last words to them. They had been, "As you found me before, so you will find me again."

"Surely we are to go on the lake and fish," said Peter. "That was how he first found us. We were out on the lake fishing all night and when we came ashore, he was there, waiting for us." He was very angry with himself for being so dense as not to have perceived this before, and he would hear of no argument from the others that what the rabbi had said was not to be taken literally.

"We must go out to fish and when we come back in the morning he will be here," he insisted.

The spring was now well advanced and the weather over the Sea of Galilee uncertain. At this time of the year the men of Capernaum did little fishing for although the sea was small, the spring gales that struck it could be even more violent than those on the Great Sea to the west. The sign of gale weather was the appearance of a ragged cloud over Mount Tabor, accompanied by a westerly wind which brought a drenching rain. Such a cloud and such a wind had been present for several days. But despite these portents of bad weather, and despite the fact that the

Capernaum fishing fleet, even the heaviest boats, had remained in harbor for a week, Peter insisted that the others put to sea with him, when they would certainly find the rabbi.

They left, then, one evening, having spent the day loading their neglected nets and overhauling the big lateen sail, which they found frayed in many places along the bolt rope where it was lashed to the yard. John was not satisfied with the repairs, particularly in view of the bad weather they could expect. He and James, from the moment Peter had said they must put to sea, had become cantankerous again and criticized all the preparations. James said the boat had been lying beached for almost two months and her seams were open and she would leak. The caulking should be inspected and the seams all payed with hot pitch.

John said plainly that he thought Peter was a fool. Why was it necessary to go out on the sea and then return to find the rabbi? The rabbi would obviously meet them on the shore and going out to sea and coming back again wouldn't bring him there any quicker.

But Peter could be as stubborn as they and said that if they didn't want to come, he could handle the boat alone and would go by himself. They knew that he could, though it would be dangerous, so with no good grace they decided to go with him.

Now when the other fishermen heard that Peter's boat was to set out that evening, some of them started to get their own boats ready, thinking that there might be a repetition of the catch of fish in which they could share. Four boats then set out when Peter eased his craft out from under the lee of the hills. But beyond that shelter, the surface of the lake was whitened with cat's paws of wind, flinging down viciously from the hills, and the waves were so rough that it was plain nobody could let down a net. The others then returned, but Peter went on to the middle of the lake, far from the shelter of the land, and he was soon in difficulties.

James and John had been right about the condition of the boat. Her planking worked in the turmoil of the sea and the caulking, dried by the sun, came loose. Soon she was leaking heavily, and the worst leak was on the garboard strake where it joined the keel. This proved so bad that bailing could not keep up with it, and James went over the side into the roaring water, taking a cape with him which he managed to wrap under the hull from one side to the other, and this helped to reduce the leak though they had to bail constantly.

The sky was overcast and the night so dark that the fishermen could not even see the waters around them, except when a wave, running down on them, exploded at its crest and hurled in a vicious cataract of boiling white upon the boat. The impact of these crests, when they struck the sides of the boat, made a noise like thunder and shook the whole hull, so that the mast vibrated in its rigging and threatened time and again to fall. The westerly wind increased toward midnight, and since the big lateen sail had been taken down at the first vicious blast, the boat was without any control, driven by wind and wave to the east shore, which was full of reefs and against which the boat would be broken and splintered.

The thunder of the seas and the moan and shriek of the wind made talk impossible and the three men fought to keep the boat afloat and check its drift onto the reefs. They got the stone anchor over the bow and let out all the scope of the anchor rode. But in the heaving and violence of the sea, the anchor dragged. They took the lateen halyards and the sheets of the sail and, tying these to the anchor rode, lengthened it to give the anchor more chance of purchase.

They could not tell, in the darkness, whether the anchor was holding or not. The boat's head came around to meet the wind and the sea, but the storm continued, and now thunder and lightning accompanied it, the blinding jagged cracks of the lightning illuminating the whole sea for a second. It was a sea, they were sure, such as had not been seen since the deluge when the whole world had been submerged in roiling water. The boat became heavier, for the cloak James had wrapped around the bottom was torn away by the action of the waves. Even if the hull had not been leaking, more water would have come aboard from the waves and the lashing rain than they could cope with.

James stopped bailing and started to inflate some goatskins to float them in the water. He passed one to Peter, who was trying to stare through the murk downwind looking for a flash of dirty white in the darkness which would tell him that they were close on the reefs. Peter ignored the goatskin and suddenly cried, "Rabbi! Master!" and jumped over the side of the boat.

James, who was near, reached to grab him, expecting to see Peter disappear in the rioting crests. But instead Peter first fell to his hands and knees in the sea, and then, getting up, as if he were ashore, ran away from the ship amidst the fury of the waves, now lost behind a comber and now reappearing, not just his head, but his whole figure, his sea cloak whipped around him by the wind, his beard and hair flung before him like seaweed.

Then they saw the rabbi beyond Peter, himself walking

over the anger of the seas, but untroubled by the wind or the rain which did not even disturb his robes. The rabbi stopped and Peter stopped too, amazed, and then, frightened, gave one terrified look back at the boat, now a hundred yards from him. Then he started to sink. A wave, its back glittering even in the darkness, flung itself down on him and over him, exploding with a thundering hiss, and despite the fury of wind and sea, James and John heard Peter shriek, "Lord, save me, or I perish."

When James saw Peter engulfed by the seas, and the same wave which had submerged him roaring down on the rabbi, he seized two of the inflated skins and, stopping only to tie a line around his waist, flung himself over the side to help them. In a second he had been swept to the length of the line, but was still some distance from them. He shouted to his brother to let out more scope. Then he saw the rabbi bend and seize Peter by the waist and hold him up. The rabbi said to Peter, "Oh, you of little faith. Why did you doubt?" In that the moment the storm subsided. The water became utterly quiet and the rabbi, holding Peter under the shoulders, walked him back to the boat. James, floating on the bladders, pulled himself in on the line and tumbled dripping into the boat.

The three of them looked around in wonder at the calm sea and the quiet sky in which the stars had now appeared, and backed away from the rabbi. Peter said in a slow voice full of awe, "Truly you are the son of God, who commands the waves and the wind." But neither James nor John could say anything.

Then the rabbi, smiling, said to James, "Did you doubt me, James, that you came over with the goatskins?"

James said, "Lord, I feared for you in the fury of the water. I thought to save you."

"Forgive him, Rabbi," said John, his brother. "He will not doubt again."

"You will doubt again because you are not angels but men," said the rabbi. "The time will come when the son of man will be spit upon and reviled and led to death and you will desert him. All but John, who will be faithful to the end."

They did not understand whom he meant by this, and in the joy of being with him again they did not think about it. John alone was deeply troubled by the words but said nothing to the others. But he resolved that whatever happened, he would not leave the side of the rabbi.

CHAPTER EIGHTEEN

In the time that followed, the rabbi performed so many miracles that wherever he went he was followed by crowds not merely of hundreds but of thousands. If he appeared in any town, whether in Galilee or in Peraea, all work stopped immediately, the women leaving their houses and the men their businesses, either in their shops or in the fields, to gather around him. This provided an immense policing problem for the senior centurion at Capernaum whose men, in their various posts, had to police these crowds so that their other duties had to be neglected.

There was, however, one marked difference between these crowds and those who had followed other leaders, and that was that they were always orderly. None of the bickering, squabbling, pushing and at times violence that marked other gatherings ever took place. The personality of the rabbi produced a gentleness among the people which was quite foreign to their aggressive, argumentative nature. This was all the more remarkable because the people who thronged about the rabbi were those who formed the unruly element among the Jews. They were coarse and uneducated, though, both by their living conditions and by their work, and doomed to continuing poverty on earth and eternal suffering when they died, for since they could not read the Law they could not fulfill its requirements and so had no hope of heaven.

The wonders the rabbi worked were of such profusion as to be beyond anything in the centurion's experience. The rabbi had only to speak and the blind saw, lepers were cured, the paralyzed could walk and the deaf could hear and the dumb speak. There were far too many of these miracles for Longinus to be in any doubt about them, though none had been performed in his presence. The rabbi, the centurion learned, performed these wonders only among the Jews, and had refused to work them for the Gentiles who were not the chosen ones. But that did not detract from their authenticity, which was vouched for by some of his own soldiers. Skeptical as he often was about miracle workers, the centurion had a good mind and realized that far from it being a confession of madness to believe in these miracles it was rather a confession of madness not to believe in them, because there were so many and they were attested to by scores of witnesses.

At second-hand he knew of one striking miracle. There was a man named Bar Timeus, the son of Timeus who came from Jericho and who had been living for many years at Capernaum. He was blind and begged for his living on the roadside, being taken to a particular spot each day to beg by a woman who had pity on him. The centurion knew him well and used him as a source of information as he used many of the beggars throughout his district. Although the man could see nothing, his hearing was acute and he could identify people by their voices.

Bar Timeus was about forty years of age. Unlike many

blind beggars, he did not revile those who failed to give him anything. Instead, when a coin was dropped into his bowl, or a bundle of food put beside him, he inquired the name of the donor and called on God to witness the charity and bless the person who had given him something.

He was the blindest man the centurion had ever seen, for his eyelids, though open, revealed eyes which were pure white, having no iris or pupil. They were like two marble stones. Once the centurion himself stopped by the man and put a half a drachma in his bowl. Bar Timeus immediately inquired the name of the donor and was informed "Longinus, the centurion."

Then Bar Timeus said, "Behold, the wolf has come to the succor of the stricken lamb. Blessed are you, soldier of the Gentiles, for God has moved your heart and you will find salvation." This impulsive act of charity by Longinus, however, rebounded on Bar Timeus. He had accepted the unclean money of a Gentile and a Roman, and very few thereafter gave him anything so that for a while he fell on hard times.

Then, while Longinus was away, for he had often to be away from Capernaum, the rabbi passed through the town and Balba, who had been left in command, reported what happened.

"There was the usual crowd about the rabbi, who was preaching as he always does," said Balba. "Bar Timeus kept calling out 'Jesus, son of David, have mercy on me,' and making such a row that the people couldn't hear the rabbi. They got angry with him and told him to shut up and the situation began to look a little ugly. I went around to see what was the trouble and Bar Timeus started shouting again and I told him that if he didn't hold his tongue, I'd make him dumb as well as blind.

"Still he wouldn't be quiet, but kept calling out, 'Jesus son of David, have mercy on me,' until the rabbi stopped his preaching and asked who it was that called to him. They told him it was Bar Timeus and he was a trouble-maker for he had taken money that was unclean." At this point Balba permitted himself a grin, for Longinus had at times reprimanded him about washing and it was gratifying, under cover of making an official report, to refer to the centurion himself as unclean.

"Go on," said the Longinus.

"Well, the rabbi called out to Bar Timcus to come to him and the people who had been hissing him down and telling him to shut his head changed their tune in an instant. I tell you, centurion, it makes you sick the way these damned Jews turn in an instant. They're like weather cocks, swinging around whatever way the wind blows. They have no loyalty to anyone and don't think for themselves . . ."

"Go on," said the centurion grimly.

"All right. But they are no good. I wouldn't trust them any further than I could throw a feather, I'll tell you that. One day they'll turn on this rabbi of theirs and tear him to pieces."

"Your report," said Longinus.

"All right. The same people who had been shushing Bar Timeus up and shaking their fists in his blind face said, sweet as blackbirds, 'Take courage. Get up. He is calling you.' So Bar Timeus flung off the old cloak he keeps over him and flung his money bowl away and started groping his way through the crowd and would have missed the rabbi altogether but I took him by the arm and led him to him. They wouldn't help him, of course, because he was born blind which meant he was a sinner. But I've been what they call a sinner so long that it didn't make any difference to me. I had to laugh though. I tell you he looked ridiculous, pawing around on the outside of the crowd with everybody avoiding him and getting nowhere. So I took him by the arm, as I said, and led him to the rabbi and the rabbi said to him, 'What do you want me to do for you?'

" 'Rabbi,' said Bar Timeus, only he used that other word they have for a rabbi of special authority."

"Rabboni," said the centurion.

"That's right. 'Rabboni, that I may see.' Now I was standing right next to the rabbi, closer than I am to you, and I know what I am talking about. The rabbi didn't touch him. He didn't make some mud with spittle or put his fingers on his eyes or put his hands on his face or anything at all. He just said, 'Go. Your faith has saved you.' And you know how Bar Timeus' eyes were—like the eyes in a marble statue? Well, the whole eye was formed in a twinkle and he let out a great shout that he could see but he couldn't see very well because there were tears streaming down his face. Still, when he had dried them, he could see as good as any man and he knelt down and picked up a handful of dirt and kissed it as if it was a jewel because he had never seen dirt before though he had been sitting in it for forty years. And that's the truth of the matter without anything put in that didn't happen."

Longinus thought about this for a while and then said to Balba, "Since you were so close to the rabbi and your own eyes are weak, why didn't you ask him to cure you too?"

"Me?" cried Balba. "You don't think he's going to waste himself on us, do you? Besides, I'd sooner be blind than ask anything of a Jew. It's beneath my dignity. I wouldn't disgrace myself by doing it."

Later Longinus saw Bar Timeus and confirmed personally that he was no longer blind. Indeed it was Bar Timeus who sought him out to thank him for the money he had given him when he was begging.

"God will remember your charity," he said. Then he fell to studying the centurion's face and Longinus thought this was because the details of a man's face were still fascinating to one blind from birth. But Bar Timeus looked sad and said, "Centurion, the road ahead is hard for you—harder than it ever was for me in my blindness. Keep your courage up and may God have mercy on you."

Thinking that Bar Timeus, in his years of begging, had overheard some plot, the centurion pressed him for an explanation of his warning. But Bar Timeus would say nothing further.

CHAPTER NINETEEN

A few months after the curing of Bar Timeus, Ruafocus, the servant of the centurion, became ill but at first Longinus did not pay much attention to his ailment. The old man was subject to fits of depression during which he talked endlessly of his home and his people who were now gone and wept openly and without shame. Nothing could ever be done to lift him from these fits and they had to be endured. Sometimes Balba would give him wine, and he would become very drunk but still talk on of his people and continue with his weeping. Then he would be enveloped by a shroud of silence during which he spoke to no one, heard no one, would not eat or stir from his bed which was in the servant's quarters of the post. His bodily functions ceased during these periods and he seemed impervious to heat or cold, lying on his bed as if dead, and refusing to eat.

Occasionally in this condition it helped to bleed him, it being apparent that some malevolence had entered his body which would be let out with the blood. At other times a cord was tied tightly around his head until it sank into the flesh. This remedy the centurion had learned from a physician from the southern regions of the Nile and its purpose was to prevent the life of the man, which was situated in the brain, escaping by slipping from the brain down through the mouth and nostrils.

When, on this occasion, Ruafocus became ill, Longinus expected that the illness would pass as it had done before. For three days then Ruafocus lay on his bed attended by the physician of the post, and the centurion had time to look in at him only in the evenings when he was through with his work. But gradually Longinus became concerned and a darkness akin to fear took possession of him.

At first this fear was only a vague feeling of anxiety as if he, the centurion, had left undone some important duty which would bring him into disfavor. It was only slowly that he began to realize that his concern centered around the illness of Ruafocus. He feared that Ruafocus would die and he shrank from thinking of the loneliness that would then lie ahead for him.

They had been together now thirty years, master and servant, and what had once been two lives had become one. The centurion had never been conscious of any affection for Ruafocus, such for instance as he felt for Balba, who was a Roman like himself and whom he had contrived to keep in service as a kindness despite his failing eyesight. What lay between the two was familiarity and the passage of thirty years spent together in a kind of exile mutually shared. The thought of being without Ruafocus was dreadful to face, and he thrust it from his mind. But as the man became weaker and weaker, the illness lasting longer than it had ever done before, the centurion's fears grew and he had Ruafocus brought from the servant's quarters and laid in his own bed. Then he sat himself at the foot of the bed, keeping a brazier burning through the night, and at times he wept.

Seeing that, under the ministrations of the camp physicians, Ruafocus was still sinking into his sickness, the centurion undertook to care for him himself. He had some skill in medicine and he washed him in warm oil to give heat to his body, and dressed him in his own clothes and put his own robes over him. He burned herbs on the brazier to purify the air and made a broth of chicken fat and honey which he tried to get down the servant's throat but without success. Then he called the subofficer of the post who had the duties of chaplain and gave him money to buy a young bull to sacrifice to the gods as a prayer that Ruafocus would recover.

This being of no avail, he called at the synagogue and asked that the Jews there, if their religion permitted it, would prey for the recovery of the Gentile. But the rabbi told him that no such prayer would be of any effect for Ruafocus was not one of the chosen ones of their god. Nor could they accept any gifts for their god from the centurion because such gifts would be unclean.

"You have been a friend to our people in helping us rebuild the synagogue," said the rabbi, "and we pity you. It is not hardness of our hearts that prevents us praying for your servant. But as I say, such prayers would be of no avail."

Longinus then thought of going to the rabbi of Nazareth as his only hope, but Balba strongly advised him against it.

"You will lose your authority if you go to him," he said. "He is a Jew. He cannot help you because you are a Gentile and he will rub that in your face before all the people present. They will make a great mock about a Roman coming to one of their own rabbis for help and if the story gets back to Pilate it will be the worse for you.

Romans do not ask help from these people. Come, centurion, you have seen death many a time. Brace yourself and accept it."

But Longinus could not accept it and thought more and more of the rabbi of Nazareth, who was markedly different from the other rabbis in that he associated freely with those held unclean. He wondered whether the rabbi, if he the centurion petitioned him though a Gentile, would heal his servant.

A few days later, a little before dawn, Ruafocus, who had been unconscious, regained his senses and called to the centurion, who was sleeping in a cot beside him.

"What is it?" asked Longinus. "I am here."

"Pay your debt now, Roman, or I die," said Ruafocus. He spoke in the language of his own people.

"Would that I could pay it," said the centurion. "But I do no know how."

"You owe a life," said Ruafocus. "Give it to me."

"But how?" Longinus demanded.

The other made no reply and the centurion, frightened, took the oil lamp and held it close to the mouth of Ruafocus. His breath was so slight that the flame hardly trembled. Then Longinus called to the guard to have his horse saddled and bring Balba to help him dress.

"Where are you going?" demanded Balba when he arrived.

"To the rabbi of Nazareth. Help me put on my full uniform."

"Are you out of your mind?" demanded Balba. "If you have to go to the rabbi put on Jew's clothing. Then perhaps he won't recognize you."

"Bring the breastplate with the medallions and the insignia of my rank," said the centurion. "I go to him as I am, a centurion of Rome."

He dressed in his most splendid uniform, wearing the helmet with the crest of red horsehair which was kept only for parades and a scarlet cloak designed for the same purpose. He put on a corselet of steel with bronze inlays and the medallions he had received from Britain and Gaul and the campaigning in Egypt and along the Rhine. He took a sword and the staff of his office as if he were on an official mission and, dispensing with a bodyguard, mounted his horse and galloped in the dwindling dark towards Bethsaida, where the rabbi was reported to be.

He arrived an hour after dawn and found the rabbi some miles beyond the town and already, despite the early hour, surrounded by a crowd of people to whom he was preaching. The crowd, intent on what the rabbi was saying, did not hear the approach of the horse and became aware of the centurion only when the rabbi himself stopped to look over their heads toward him.

All turned and saw the scarlet-cloaked officer in his plumed helmet coming toward them. They could see from the manner in which he was dressed and from the staff of authority which he carried in his hand that he had come on official business, and they started to move away for they were afraid that the Roman had come to arrest the rabbi as John the Baptizer had been arrested. Some of them, braver than the others, reached for stones. The centurion surprised them however by dismounting rather than riding his horse through them to the rabbi. He threw the reins over his horse's head and walked up the little hill to the rabbi and the people parted to let him through, murmuring against him.

When he was some few feet from the rabbi he stopped

and said, "Lord, I entreat of you to cure my servant who is sick. I fear he will die and we have been together thirty years. I have wronged him. Let him live even if I must die myself."

The rabbi replied, though gently, "Why do you come to me, Roman? It is not fit for the food of children to be given to others."

"Rabbi," said the centurion, "I have nowhere else to turn, and I love this man. Behold now he is dying, and I am helpless and so I come thus to you, that you may have pity on him. For you alone can help him, as all men know."

"Since you have such faith I will come to your house and cure him." He started to move then down the slope toward the centurion, but Longinus stopped him with a gesture of his hand.

"Lord," he said, "I am not worthy that you should come under my roof. Only say the word and my servant will be healed.

"For I too am a man, as you can see, who is subject to authority; and have soldiers who are subject to me. I say to one 'Go' and he goes and to another 'Come' and he comes and to my servant 'Do this' and he does it. Therefore you have only to command the sickness and it will depart from my servant."

"You so believe?" asked the rabbi.

"Rabbi," said the centurion, "how could any man doubt it?"

Then the rabbi turned to the crowd and said, "Listen well to what I say for I have not found such great faith in Israel as in this Roman. And I tell you that many will come from the east and from the west, and will feast with Abraham and Isaac and Jacob in the kingdom of heaven.

But the children of the kingdom will be put forth into the darkness outside."

He turned then to the centurion and said, "Go your way; as you have believed, so be it done unto you."

"Lord," said Longinus, "now I know that my servant will not die but is well this minute. Whatever I may do for you that is not contrary to my duty, I will do and let those who stand here bear witness to this pledge."

The rabbi looked at the centurion with great love, and said to the others, "Behold a man wrongly born who will be born again and will be remembered dearly in the prayers of men until the end of the earth." But neither Peter nor John understood those words.

When Longinus had returned to Capernaum he found Ruafocus well and about his duties.

"All that is past is now settled between us, Roman," he said. "Yet," he added mischievously, "I am ahead in the matter for I have been born again, as was told me in my dream of the wind, and you await a second birth. But it will surely come to you as it has come to me."

BOOK III

CHAPTER TWENTY

A change now began to take place among the landless people in Judaea, Galilee and Peraea across the Jordan. They had, through the years, provided the unruly element of Jewish society, having little hope of happiness either in this world or in the next. They were surly and resentful of authority—quick to gather in crowds and quick to riot. They had been a mob living always on the edge of violence and, thronging to Jerusalem during feast days, controlled the streets and taverns and shops. There was a name for them—the Rejected, and it was because of them rather than any tendency to revolt among the upper classes that three full Roman legions were stationed on garrison duty in Palestine.

In Rome, of course, there was a similar problem, the city being crowded with men who were taxed out of their farms and who in a slave society could not get gainful employment. Slaves made the shoes and the clothing and the furniture and unloaded the ships and transported the goods and built the houses, and a free man could not get work with which to earn a living. But Rome had met the problem of the mob with bread and circuses and free public baths and occasional distributions of money and goods at the hands of a conqueror, the system having being started by Julius Caesar.

But though the same system of pacifying the mob had been tried in Palestine, it did not work. It didn't work because the Palestine mob, though despairing of salvation, being ignorant of the Law or unable to fulfill its every scruple, still would not attend the gladiatorial exhibitions, the horse races, the pagan displays of Rome. They would not even make use of the free baths which were constructed in Jerusalem, in Caesarea and in Tiberias, as well as in numbers of other smaller cities throughout the land. Damned as they believed themselves to be, they would not damn themselves further by enjoying pagan entertainments and indeed they would not even live in the new city of Tiberias which was being constructed on the western shore of the Sea of Galilee.

Here they were offered good housing, good water supply, good streets and shops and they would not live in the city, first because it was a Roman city and second because in the laying of its foundations, an ancient graveyard had been uncovered. No Jew would live in a city erected over a graveyard for the whole area was unclean. And so Rome was unable to cope with the Rejected, to provide them with diversions and sublimate their smoldering anger which had its roots in a deep temporal and spiritual frustration. And Rome's only answer was more legions and more policing.

But after the coming of the rabbi of Nazareth, the attitude of the Rejected underwent a significant change. The anger of the greater part of these people subsided, to be replaced first by a passivity and then by a gentleness toward each other, such as might exist among members of an affectionate family.

The outward signs of this were trivial but the cumulative effect was great. Beggars, with whom the land abounded, divided the proceeds of their day with those so afflicted that they could not even beg. Some took food to the neglected sick and cared for them. People began to share their clothing and their miserable shelters with each other. Women began to feed and care for children who were homeless, and all this, though affecting only the lowest elements of the land, produced a contentment and happiness which had not been known among these people before and was the result both of the preaching and of the example of the rabbi of Nazareth.

The start of this change, if a start could be found for it, came from a sermon which he had preached to a mob so big that he had to leave Capernaum and go to a small mountain called the Horns of Hittim some miles to the south to accommodate the crowd.

In many respects the rabbi's preaching was quite different from that of other teachers. First, he did not preach only in the Temple but more often in the open whenever a crowd had gathered around him. Second, he never dealt with the Law, but talked about their daily lives and their Father in Heaven who looked after them so that they could feel his presence in the mountains and fields and valleys. Again he used no subtleties, but spoke directly so that there was no hidden meaning in his words. And finally he made up little stories, about planting seeds or harvesting grain or going on a journey, or losing a coin, or lighting a lamp, or building a house, all of which applied directly to their own lives. He was not at all hard to understand and nobody went away from these sermons perplexed over what he had meant and feeling frustrated and inferior because they could not understand what he said or match with their minds the brilliancy of his own.

Also he seemed, unlike other teachers, to care for each one of them individually and not to hold himself in the tiniest degree above them. He never displayed any learning that they had not themselves and he often made them smile with talk of the work of farming or fishing or building. He knew something about all these things—the heat in the vineyards during the grape harvest and the weariness of the hands and shoulders in truing up a stone for a building or a wall. He did not mind being crowded and touched and pulled at. He didn't think this made him unclean. He sat down and ate with them in the open, without first performing an elaborate washing, or inquiring where the food came from, or insuring that the hands of those who touched it had been purified. And he often slept in the open, as they did too, finding some hollow or shelter in a cave and wrapping his robe around him.

He was their rabbi, speaking personally to each one of them; not condemning them but encouraging them and often, when they listened to him, they bowed their heads to hide the tears that came because there was someone at last who cared for them.

When the vast crowd had assembled that day on the Horns of Hittim, and had become silent, the rabbi himself said nothing for a while but looked them over with compassion. They were indeed the Rejected—the poorest of the land. Their clothing was torn and patched. They did not have sandals on their feet. They were thin and hungry and unwashed but they looked at him with tremendous expectation, as if convinced that he would tell them something special on this occasion which would sustain them through all their hardships yet to come.

He quoted no text and told them no little story, but speaking as if to each one individually and with great sincerity said, "Blessed are you poor, for yours is the kingdom of God.

"Blessed are you who hunger now, for you shall be satisfied. Blessed are you who weep now, for you shall laugh.

"Blessed are you who hunger and thirst for justice, for you shall have your fill.

"Blessed are you who are merciful, for you shall obtain mercy.

"Blessed are you who are clean of heart, for you shall see God.

"Blessed are you who make peace among your neighbors, for you shall be called the children of God.

"Blessed are you who suffer persecution but will not renounce what is right, for yours is the kingdom of heaven.

"Blessed are you when men reproach you and persecute you and speaking falsely, say all manner of evil against you, for my sake. Rejoice and exult, because your reward is great in heaven; for so did they persecute the prophets who were before you."

Before he started talking to the crowd in this manner, they had been silent. But that silence seemed as a tumult now compared with the utter stillness that came on them as they listened to each word. Even the wind seemed not to stir through the coarse grasses around, and not a child moved, for it was as if all were under a spell, so deep was the effect of these words on them.

"You have heard the Law 'An eye for an eye' and 'A tooth for a tooth,'" the rabbi continued. "But I give you a new law. Do not resist the evildoer, but on the contrary, if someone strikes you on the cheek, turn to him the other cheek. If anyone would take you to court to sue for your tunic, give him your cloak as well. If someone forces you against your will to walk a mile with him, go of your free will a further mile with him. If someone asks you for food or shelter or money, give these things to him gladly. If someone asks to borrow from you, do not turn him away. The old law says 'Thou shalt love thy neighbor and shalt hate thine enemy.' Again I give you a new law: Love your enemies, do good to those who hate you and pray for those who ill-treat you and tell lies about you. If you love only those who love you, what virtue is there in that? Even the worst of men love those who love them. If you have a kind word only for your own friends, what virtue is there in that? Have a kind word for the stranger and the outcast and that will bring a smile to your Father's face.

"When you help someone who needs help, do not tell everybody about it. If you do so, you have already had your reward. When you give a little money to someone who is in need, be so quiet about it that your left hand does not know that your right hand has given the money. But God will know and he will reward you. Do not criticize the faults of others, and tell other people how to reform themselves. Look for your own faults and change your own conduct. For your own faults may be much greater than those you see in your neighbors."

He spoke for a long time in this manner so that it was midafternoon when he had finished, and then those in the crowd who were afflicted in some way, being either blind or lame or dumb, and some indeed paralyzed and carried on stretchers, begged him to cure them, and he did, always laying his hands upon them though some were horrid with ulcers.

Towards lepers he was particularly tender, because of all the Rejected, these were the most rejected. A party of them came up the hill toward him, crying out, "Unclean, unclean," as commanded by law and the people moved away, some of the shouting to the lepers to come no closer. But still they came on, like cadavers crawling from the grave, toward the rabbi.

Two among them, a man and a child, were so far gone in the disease that they had no legs but only horrifying glistening stumps. The child was on a wooden sled, being pulled by another leper who had a cloth like a shroud wrapped across his face to hide his disfigurement. The man achieved locomotion with his arms, dragging his torso along by grabbing at rocks and roots. Three were blind and were roped together and led by another and this procession of horror came toward the rabbi while those around him moved away moaning.

The ground was rough and when the lepers were still some distance off, the wooden sled on which the child was being pulled tipped over and the child rolled a little way down the hill, like a bag of old rags but making no sound, for children who were lepers soon learned that crying or whimpering was of no avail to them.

The man who was pulling the sled went after the child, but had difficulty lifting it up onto the sled for his arms were quite useless. The others had gone on, fearful lest if they delayed the rabbi might move away and their opportunity would be lost. Peter saw the man struggling with the child and shouted angrily to the other lepers to help him, but they paid no attention, only striving to come faster lest the rabbi depart for it was now dusk.

Peter, without thinking what he was doing, ran to the child and picked it up, though the stench nauseated him.

He came back to the rabbi as quickly as he could, to be rid of his burden, fearful of the breath of the child in his face and the touch of its arms around his neck. He got to the rabbi ahead of the rest of the lepers and, everybody but John having moved back, he stood there, the child still in his arms.

The rabbi was smiling, a little smile which had a suggestion of teasing in it. "Peter," he asked, "why do you bring me the child?"

"Lord," said Peter, "that you may cure it."

"How great is your faith, Peter?" the rabbi asked.

"When I do not think, Lord," said Peter, "it is without limit. But when I think I am full of doubts."

"What causes you to doubt, Peter?" the rabbi persisted.

"It is because I know myself, Lord. I am a sinful man and weak and there is no goodness in me."

"Peter," said the rabbi, "when such thoughts occur to you, remember I have not come to strengthen the strong, but to strengthen the weak. Therefore, now, call on your Father and cure the child yourself in his name."

"Father," said Peter, "if it be your will, cure this child, and do not take into account my worthiness."

He could never explain what happened next. He knew only that the earth beneath him seemed to shake a little, or perhaps the sky moved, as if he were dizzy. Then the child was out of his arms and standing on the ground, its legs and feet perfectly restored. The child looked at him for one astonished moment, and then throwing its arms around his waist buried its head in his robes, weeping. In the next second it had gone, darting down the mountainside; and taking the armless leper who had been dragging it on the sled, led him to Peter. But Peter said, "Not I.

Not I. But the son of God himself, who is among us," and pointed to the rabbi.

"You have spoken truly," said the rabbi. "And no one has revealed this to you but the Father. Peter is your name and signifies rock. And you are the rock, Peter, on which I will build my church, and the gates of hell shall not prevail against it."

The rabbi then turned to the other lepers, of whom there were nine, and asked them what they wanted of him. And those of them who could speak said, "Rabbi, that we may be made whole."

He then went to each one and touched him and said, "Let it be done to you according to your belief," and each one was cured.

The news of these cures soon spread through the whole land, and even up to the country of Canaan to the north and Egypt to the south.

With this news went a report of the teaching of the rabbi on the Horns of Hittim, the new doctrine he had given for salvation, which did not concern itself with the strict rituals of the Law. So it was that there was a new spirit among the people, particularly among the lowest segments, and crowds of them followed him wherever he went, so that he often had to escape from them by going deep into the wilderness or crossing the Sea of Galilee in the boat either of Peter or of the sons of Zebedee.

The news also reached Pilate and the high priests Annas and Caiphas. Pilate was delighted at the authority of the Pharisees being shaken by the preaching of the rabbi. But the high priests were concerned and consulted with the Sanhedrin as to what should be done to remove the threat posed by the rabbi to their authority.

CHAPTER TWENTY-ONE

Caiphas, who was known as the Roman High Priest because of his appointment by Pilate, had an ambitious and subtle mind, qualities that commended themselves to Pilate, who was himself known as "The Fox." Representing the Roman influence in the affairs of the Temple, he was, at first, distrusted by the scribes and the elders, and reckoned a menace.

But the struggle in the inner councils of the Temple was not merely a two-sided one between Annas and Caiphas, but involved also a deeper struggle between the two religious parties into which the Jews were divided.

There was actually not one Sanhedrin but two, reflecting this division. One had civil authority and one religious authority. This latter, though it had fewer members, was called "The Great Sanhedrin" and had its offices in the Temple itself. It was under the direct leadership of the High Priest Annas, and its members were for the greater part Sadducees. These held that only the written Law, given by God to Moses, was binding on the people, and all else, including the preachings of the prophets of Israel, was mere tradition handed down by word of mouth and was not binding. In this they were opposed by the Pharisees, which was the growing party and which controlled the lesser Sanhedrin which met in chambers outside the Temple in the city of Jerusalem itself. The Pharisees held the words of the prophets as binding as the Law of Moses. To this they had added innumerable interpretations, all equally binding, so that such a mass of scruple of observance accummulated that it was impossible for a man in the course of ordinary living to fulfill the requirements for salvation as laid down by the Pharisees.

Men might atone for their failings, however, by making offerings at the Temple. Certain offerings were laid down by the original law or by tradition, but others came into being for further atonement and all those offerings enriched the Temple, in either coin or goods, or in the sale of sacrificial animals or the sale of the carcasses of animals which had been killed in sacrifice.

Pilate had inquired fully into the difference between Pharisee and Sadducee, seeking always to divide the allegiance of the people. The Pharisees he learned were originally reckoned "the exiles" or "outcasts," which was what the name implied. But they were zealous and definite and vigorous and had the greatest influence among the people, because of their vigor. Excluded as outcasts from the Great Sanhedrin of the high priest, they had many years before established their own Sanhedrin exercising civil control. They penetrated the synagogues, tried to extend their already considerable influence in the Temple, opposed the Greater Sanhedrin, composed of Sadducees, though subtly, and in so doing, opposed the high priest himself.

Into this situation Pilate had inserted the second high priest, Caiphas, and Caiphas courted the Pharisees having no hope of support elsewhere. Both Caiphas and the

Pharisees stood to gain from an alliance. By supporting Caiphas, the Pharisees could extend their influence in the councils of the Temple and its government. By supporting the Pharisees, Caiphas could make himself secure in his office, having the majority religious party on his side.

Pilate came to think of Annas as the Sadducee High Priest and Caiphas as the Pharisee High Priest, and this division pleased him though he would have been happier to have seen the Sadducees more powerful. They were indeed the party which was friendlier to Rome. Annas lived in luxury, in a house constructed on the lines of a Greco-Roman villa. He was not puritanical in his views, entertained Roman officers, gave big feasts, and in the privacy of his house dressed like a Roman and dismissed the scruples of religious observance. Inclining to the view of the Sadducees, he looked for no Messiah and his main concern was to see that the people remained docile and gave no offense to Rome. He knew the love of his people for prophets and workers of miracles, and never uttered a word against either John the Baptizer or the rabbi from Nazareth, who now had a far greater following than John.

But Caiphas, looking for support from the Pharisees, had to be concerned with the rabbi from Nazareth, for both in his preaching and in his behavior he contradicted the doctrines of the Pharisees. The Pharisee Sanhedrin saw the loss of its authority over the people in the new rabbi, and a secret meeting was held to decide what was to be done. Caiphas was present at this meeting, and Annas too, but Annas came only to keep himself informed of the decisions of the Pharisees.

He found one decision already made—the rabbi must be removed. The business to be discussed was not whether this should be done, but how it should be done, and Annas protested this prejudgment of the rabbi. "What has he done that is contrary to any law?" he asked. "I hear no reports of blasphemy or conspiracy on his part. I hear of no riots he has led. I have not heard of him speaking against the authority of the Temple or of the authority of Rome. I hear only that he works miracles and does good among the people. What are the grounds for the decision to remove him?"

"He sets himself up as the Messiah," said Caiphas.

Annas smiled slyly. "But since, my dear Caiphas, you are of the party that believes there will be a Messiah, why do you object to this?"

"Because he is a false Messiah. He does not follow the rituals concerning purification. He defiles himself every day in his eating and in the society he keeps. He is a rabble rouser, seeking his support from the most irresponsible section of the people, who will lead them in a revolt against Rome, for which all will suffer. It is better that one man, this self-appointed rabbi who is the son of a builder of Nazareth, die than that the whole nation be put to the sword."

"Has he been heard preaching insurrection?" asked Annas.

"Whether he has preached it or not, that is the logical end of his mission," said Caiphas. "The mob he leads now will soon take control of him. There will be an insurrection whether he wishes it or not. And the punishment will descend on our heads, for you know that the Romans will insist that this is not a section of our people revolting, but all our people."

Seeing them thus determined, Annas said nothing more. The meeting began to discuss how the rabbi could be trapped. With such multitudes around him at all times, he could not be taken in the daytime. He would have to be taken when he was alone, or with only his disciples about him. It was the young rabbi Saul, whose Roman name was Gaius Julius Paulus, who suggested that it might be possible to find one among the disciples of the rabbi who would betray him.

"There are twelve of them," he said. "It would be contrary to human nature if among twelve men one could not be found who is not disloyal. Money will be required but no great amount of money, for these are not men accustomed to riches."

"If he is taken, however," said another, "of what charge is he to be accused? What evidence have we that we can bring against him?"

"Exactly," said Annas. "What harm has he done?"

"And who among the crowds that surround him will testify against him even if he has preached sedition?" asked another.

"We will get our own evidence against him," said Caiphas. "We will send members from this council to question him publicly on both points of the Law and points of obedience to Rome."

But not all who were present agreed with this. "We should be wary," said one, "that we are not setting a snare for an innocent man. What we are doing here is plotting against a man against whom no charge can be brought at present except that the multitudes love him. We doom him ahead of any crime on his part and that is contrary to the commandment of God."

"That is not so," said Caiphas angrily. "What wrong is there in questioning a man publicly on his beliefs? What wrong is there when a man is suspected of sedition in dragging his real motives out of him? If this rabbi were not plotting an insurrection, why has he not come honestly to us here and stated his mission and his doctrine before the Sanhedrin? If he is the Messiah, why has he not come to us, as the authorities over the people, and plainly stated so and given us a sign as proof? Has he sought out Annas or me or any of you? No. On the contrary he has avoided us all and confined his preaching and his wonder-working to an ignorant and credulous country population.

"We who have studied the Law well know that a little learning among the ignorant is a dangerous thing. Anyone who can as much as read the Torah can interpret it according to his own desires, and point to word and verse to prove his interpretation, and it is because of this that we have rabbinical schools, studying the Law in its greatest depth, so that the correct interpretation of each passage is brought forth.

"At what school did this rabbi study—at that of Gamaliel, or of Bar Joseph, or of Bar Hillel? At none. He is his own interpreter of the Torah, and with his interpretation he is distorting our Law and destroying the faith of our people."

"And yet in curious ways, he himself fulfills much of what has been prophesied regarding the Messiah," said another. "He was born in Bethlehem, of the House of David, and comes from Nazareth, as was foretold of the Messiah."

"Wonderful," said Caiphas with sarcasm. "The whole of Nazareth is of the House of David, and every pregnant woman in Nazareth was compelled at the time of the census of Augustus to go to Bethlehem to register. Wasn't Bethlehem at that time so overcrowded that people were sleeping in the streets and in stables? I could find you a score of men in Nazareth alive this day who on that definition could claim to be the Messiah. If this rabbi is the Messiah would it be hidden from us, the priests of the people? Would it be known to filthy beggars and day laborers and unknown to us who serve God daily in the Temple and observe every detail of the Law?

"If that is so, then we who serve God have been thrown aside by God in favor of the dogs in the street.

"No, when God sends the Messiah, he will not hide him, but all will know who he is, and his first announcement of his mission will surely be made to the high priests and to the elders."

With such arguments Caiphas and his supporters finally prevailed on the meeting to send selected doctors of the Law to question the rabbi and trap him. Among those selected were Saul and another Simon, who was from Capernaum. And it was also agreed that the rabbi's disciples should be approached to see if there was not one among them who would betray him for money or some other consideration.

But this agreement was not unanimous. Some reserved their judgment on the rabbi. Some opposed the decision which they found a conspiracy against an innocent man. Caiphas made a note of these with the object of insuring that they were excluded from further meetings on the matter. But some of them sent a warning to the rabbi of these deliberations.

These warnings were not given directly to the rabbi, for the messengers who carried them were unable to talk to him privately. They spoke, however, to his disciples, and the disciples cautioned the rabbi that the members of the Sanhedrin of the Pharisees were seeking to trap him. But he said only, "The Son of Man must suffer many things, and be rejected by the elders and chief priests and scribes, and be put to death, and on the third day rise again." But because of the wonders that he had performed, none of his disciples could believe what he said. They reasoned that he was talking in a parable which had a deeply hidden meaning, and he would explain it to them later. But from that day forward, Peter became more and more concerned about the rabbi and could not shake off his uneasiness.

CHAPTER TWENTY-TWO

A change also took place in the ministry of the rabbi after the sermon he had preached on the Horns of Hittim. He worked fewer and fewer miracles, sought to avoid the crowds that followed him everywhere and spent more time with his disciples instructing them, particularly Peter and the two sons of Zebedee, James and John.

At the start of his ministry, the rabbi had been confident and joyous, often laughing and sometimes teasing his disciples, for he had a delicate sense of humor which hurt no one and yet, when thought upon, illustrated a point.

Peter, whose sense of humor was heavier, had suspected that when the rabbi called him the rock on which he would build his church, he was teasing him. Although to the rabbi, a builder, a rock would make a good foundation for a house, to Peter, a fisherman, a rock was a hazard which could split open a boat. He suspected then that the rabbi was quietly teasing him on the weaknesses of his own nature which, like a submerged reef, menaced any great enterprise or voyage he might set out upon. He took the rabbi aside some time later and questioned him about this, asking him how he could describe as a rock a man whose resolve was often utterly shattered.

"You know me to be weak, Lord," said Peter. "John has more resolve than I."

"Therefore I chose you," said the rabbi. "For only the weak can understand the weaknesses of others and those who fall down can understand how another falls. John cannot understand the frailties of others and will be with me to the very end, but you will turn from me and deny me and suffer greatly before you return to me again. And having done so you will understand the failings of all men and will not cast out those who succumb to fear and doubts."

Peter was frightened by the rabbi's talk of the end, so frightened indeed that he sought to avoid any mention of it and did not even question the rabbi on what he meant. The rabbi, out of pity for him, did not at this time talk further of the matter.

At the beginning of his ministry the rabbi had often attended weddings and feasts of pure pleasure prepared for him by those who wanted to honor him. Among these was Levi, the tax collector at the Gate of the Flies in Capernaum. This man the rabbi had called to follow him, and Levi had immediately left his work and come after him and been given the name of Matthew. Judas of Kerioth had been troubled about the calling of Levi or Matthew to be a disciple, had spoken to Peter about it and, getting no satisfaction there, had gone to the rabbi.

"Already you have suffered in reputation by having one man of money among your disciples in myself, Rabbi," he said. "And now you have added a tax collector whom you know is more hated by the people than I, a money changer and banker. I have heard murmuring in the multitude against this. If you wish Levi called Matthew to follow you, then the scandal would be reduced if I left."

"Judas," said the rabbi. "Answer me, is the disciple greater than the master?"

"Oh no, Rabbi," cried Judas. "I had not intended to suggest that. I am only anxious that your reputation should not suffer."

"How then can the reputation of him who is greater suffer from the reputation of him who is less?" asked the rabbi. "Is the master condemned for the character of his servants? Beware, Judas, and look carefully to your own salvation, for the evil in men lies not in their occupations but in their hearts and there are many priests whose office is respected who are less worthy than tax collectors whose office is despised."

Judas trembled at this warning and went immediately to Matthew and told him all that he had said to the rabbi and begged his forgiveness. He also asked Matthew to take over the office of money handler for the rabbi, for many gifts of goods and money came to him, and these Judas had taken care of.

"Money is a scandal to me," said Judas. "It frets me and worries me and leads me astray. Will you now not take care of the money box?"

"Assuredly if it will help you," said Matthew. "Give it to me."

"Here then is the cash we use for our needs," said Judas, "and the other money is desposited and I will give you a deed giving you authority over it."

Matthew took the cash box and, there being a great multitude of people about who were following the rabbi, he opened the box and passed among them, inviting them to take all that they needed. "Pass the word to those who are still in need to return tomorrow," he said, "when I will distribute the rest of our funds."

Judas trembled in indignation at this scattering of all the rabbi's wealth, but when he went to the rabbi to complain, he found him laughing heartily. The rabbi took Matthew in his arms and kissed him and said, "Now truly, here is a miracle—a collector of taxes returning the taxes." Everybody laughed at the sally except Judas, who had kept the accounts scrupulously and with the greatest honesty and now saw all his work scattered to the winds. Although he had promised to make over the rest of the money to Matthew he retained some, reasoning that when all were hungry and needed money to buy food they would thank him. Some of the money he had indeed invested, having convinced himself that not to do so would be to deprive the rabbi and his followers of income. He was troubled because a payment on one of these investments was due and Matthew had disposed of all the available cash.

Levi was himself a wealthy man, and was one of the people who held a great feast for the rabbi shortly after his calling. He gathered all his friends to this feast—merchants and traders, many of them in the service of Rome—and served plenty of food and plenty of wine so that everybody ate well and drank with pleasure together.

The feast was held in the open portico before Levi's house so everybody could see the rabbi sitting down with such a company, and some of the Pharisees, sent to question the rabbi, saw him enjoying himself in this manner which was forbidden.

They gathered in the road before the portico, wagging their heads and drawing their robes over their faces as a sign that they were scandalized, and an uncomfortable silence settled on those at the table. Then Saul, who was among these Pharisees, called out to the rabbi, "Why do you eat and drink with publicans and sinners and others who are corrupt and unclean and yet pretend to preach the word of God? Does the servant of God sit at the table with the servants of Mammon?"

"Tell me, Saul," replied the rabbi, "your father was a physician. Who had need of his services—those who were well or those who were sick?"

"Those who were sick," replied Saul.

"Therefore," said the rabbi, "I come not to call the just to repentance, but the sinners. Or do you think that Caiphas and the members of the Sanhedrin have more need of my presence than these among whom they will not mingle even to preach the word of God?"

Saul made no answer but another said, "The disciples of John the Baptizer, who was known to all as a man of God and put to death by Herod, fast daily and pray and mortify themselves and avoid the pleasures of the flesh. So also do the disciples of the Pharisees. Why then do you and your disciples eat and drink like Gentiles, giving yourselves heartily to the pleasures of the table?"

"The disciples of John and of the Pharisees have need of fasting," replied the rabbi, "for they await the coming of one without whom the feast may not be given. But when the host of the feast has arrived, then his guests should not fast but should make merry with him and eat fully. For when he has gone, there will be time to fast indeed."

"You talk in riddles," said the Pharisee.

"Are you so learned in the Law and yet do not know to whom I refer?" asked the rabbi. "Have you spent your years poring over the Torah, debating with a score of others the significance of the last tittle only to know nothing of what you read? The blind I can cure and the deaf I can heal. But who can heal those who, though not blind, will not see, and those who, though not deaf, will not hear? I tell you you are blind with your own blindness and deaf with your own deafness and therefore cure yourselves or fall into the pit."

When his questioners had withdrawn, the rabbi signaled to the wine steward, who commenced to fill the cups of the guests. And while this was being done, the rabbi, watching the wine being poured from the containers which were made from the stomach of a goat, said, "No one pours new wine into old wineskins; else the new wine will burst the old skins and will be split, and the skins ruined. But new wine must be put into fresh skins and both are saved. Therefore I invite you to drink of my new wine and be yourselves the skins that will contain it."

As time went by the rabbi began to perceive that many, particularly among the wealthy people, were more impressed by his miracles than by his words and he became sad and attended fewer and fewer feasts. The greater part of the people, even among the Rejected, spoke of him as a wonder worker, a magician, rather than a teacher. He worked then fewer cures and began to talk of his forthcoming end as if it had become plain to him that he must die for his mission to succeed. He told Peter, James and John that it was now necessary that he should be put to death but they would not believe this and Peter begged the rabbi not to talk of such matters. Peter decided that the rabbi was overtired, and indeed once he had complained that the foxes and birds of the air had places to rest, but he had nowhere to lay down his head. But it was Andrew who really understood the rabbi.

His character was not as complex as Peter's. He did

not spend so much time on self-examination and self-doubt as his brother, but accepted things as they came along, doing his best in whatever circumstances surrounded him. He was the younger of the brothers and as is so often the case, had profited from seeing the enthusiasms and depressions to which Peter was subject and this had made him steadier and slower to speak his feelings. He explained to the others that the rabbi had concluded that he was not fulfilling his mission by preaching and by curing. Many came to him and believed in him. But others came only to see wonders and many openly doubted that he was sent from God, even after seeing cures before their own eyes. They sought other explanations, even going to the extent of saying that the cures were obtained through the devil rather than through God.

"I believe," said Andrew, "that he has decided that he must be put to death, and then he will raise himself from the dead, and then surely all the world will believe in him, and will follow him."

"But if he wants all to believe in him, he has only to command them to do so." said John. "He could make Pilate or Herod believe in him. What is holding him back?"

"He has already told us that there are none so blind as those who will not see," said Andrew quietly. "The rabbi wants willing belief, for men have free will. He will not command belief. And as for dying has he not already told us that the good shepherd is the one who will die for his flock? And so he speaks of dying for us, who follow him as sheep."

"I will die for him rather than have him die for me," cried Peter. "I will not let anyone put a hand on him—not even Pilate's men."

"There will be no need of anyone dying," said John. "He will, when he is ready, perform one miracle so great that all men, willing or not, must believe in him or confess themselves insane."

That miracle came with the raising of Lazarus from the dead. Lazarus, the brother of Mary and Martha of Bethany, had been three days in the tomb when the rabbi, summoned, came to Bethany and heard that Lazarus, whom he loved, was already dead.

Some criticized the rabbi for letting his friend die and whispered that he had come too late. "He could cure the blind and the deaf and the lepers," they said. "He knew beforehand that Lazarus was sick, but did nothing. Now it is too late. He did not save his friend when he could, and that is why he weeps," for the rabbi wept at the news that Lazarus was in the tomb.

The rabbi, however, was taken to the tomb and stood before it and said to Martha, "Have them take away the stone that seals the door."

"Lord," said Martha, "my brother has been buried four days and is already decayed."

The rabbi replied, "Have I not told you already that if you believe you will see the wonders God can work? What is four days of death to the power of God who created all life? Have them move aside the stone."

Martha then ordered this done, and the rabbi raised his eyes to heaven and cried out, "Father, I give you thanks that you have heard me. I know, Father, that you always hear me but I speak now that those who stand here doubting may believe that you have sent me to them."

Everybody heard this and looked to the dark hole of the tomb from which came a sickening odor of the decay mixed with the oil of anointment. The rabbi also looked at the tomb and cried in a commanding voice so that all could hear his words, "Lazarus, I bid you come forth."

In the darkness and silence of the tomb through which these words echoed, they saw a vague white shape move. It stumbled forward, a blind, groaning figure, swaddled in funeral wrappings so that it could take only the smallest of steps. The crowd groaned and those in front fell on their knees and covered their heads, but those behind, who could not at first see, stretched themselves to watch what was happening. A shaft of sunlight slanted across the door of the tomb and out of the darkness and into this sunlight came the figure of Lazarus, every part of him covered in the cloths of burial. None now stood but the rabbi and Peter and John and the two sisters of Lazarus, Mary and Martha. To these the rabbi said, "Unbind him from the cloths and let him go."

Mary and Martha, sobbing, ripped the cloths from their brother, and when his face was clear of them, he saw the rabbi and struggled toward him and said, "I was with others, waiting for you, Lord."

But the rabbi said, "Speak nothing of that until the time has come."

This miracle was witnessed by several hundred people, including some of the scribes and Pharisees. But when the Pharisees who had witnessed the miracle reported to Caiphas and the Less or Civil Sanhedrin, Caiphas was beside himself with rage.

"Has he deceived even you?" he demanded of the Pharisees who brought him the report. "Are you also Galileans now? This whole thing is a trick, played by this Jesus and Lazarus who are closest friends. Lazarus was not dead at all, but only pretending to be. This rabbi is an imposter and he must die and Lazarus too."

A great many of the Pharisees then withdrew from the Sanhedrin, but those that remained were all the more determined to put the rabbi to death.

When the rabbi heard of Caiphas' reaction to the raising of Lazarus he fell silent for a day. Then he began to talk more often of being put to death himself. Peter pleaded with him to avoid Judaea and Jerusalem. But the rabbi said, "When the time comes, I must take up my cross and you yours."

CHAPTER TWENTY-THREE

Judas of Kerioth had been present at the raising of Lazarus from the dead and also had listened while Andrew suggested that perhaps the rabbi himself intended to die so that he could also be raised from the dead when no one would then doubt him. He thought a great deal about this. He knew that Andrew, for all his quietness, had a good analytical mind, and he privately drew up a list of the miracles that the rabbi had worked since the time he knew him. They included cures of every kind and one other raising from the dead at Naim, when the rabbi had, out of compassion, called back to life the son of a widow who was strapped to a pallet and on his way to burial. Judas had not been a witness to all these miracles but only to some of them. But he had seen many and marveled at them.

It was plain that the rabbi had complete power over all things and over all conditions. That he could however raise himself from the dead was a matter of grave doubt in the mind of Judas. How, he asked himself, could a man, dead, have any power, since death was that condition in which all power had departed? Certainly no ordinary man could raise himself from the dead. Not even

Moses had done so, nor Abraham, who was the father of the nation, nor Isaiah nor Daniel nor any of the prophets. If indeed the rabbi could achieve the impossible and raise himself from the dead, then he was clearly no ordinary man, or even merely a prophet, but the Messiah and the Son of God Himself. Peter, Philip, James, John, Bar Timeus, whom he had cured of blindness—all the others accepted him as the Messiah and the Son of God but Judas could not. He reflected that many of the others had had the benefit of a miracle preceding their conversion but he had had none. Even Nathaniel had had a little miracle performed, for the rabbi had known his name, though a stranger, and called him by his name while he was standing under a fig tree. That had been enough miracle for Nathaniel.

Judas wondered whether the greatest of all miracles was not reserved for him: in short the death of the rabbi and his return alive from the grave.

The rabbi had said that the last would be first and the first would be last, and this had made a singular impression on the mind of Judas. If he took a hand in bringing about the death and return to life of the rabbi, he would no longer be (as he felt) a little despised among the disciples, and the least of them, but greatly honored, for it would certainly appear that his faith had been greater than theirs. He would have put it to the test, by helping to bring about the death of the rabbi, knowing that he would rise again. And if on the other hand, the rabbi did not rise again, he would have performed a great service both to the rabbi and to Israel by demonstrating that he was not the Messiah but only a prophet of extraordinary powers, and the people must wait for another. Whichever way the matter fell out, he would be honored for having performed a real service.

The thought of betraying the rabbi occurred to him more frequently after he learned that Caiphas had promised a reward for such a betrayal. He began to toy with it and reflect that what on the surface appeared a betrayal would actually be a great service to the rabbi and to Israel. Perhaps, however, he would never have decided to go through with such a plan, holding it only in his mind as a matter for contemplation but not for action, if he was not now being pressed for money.

He had invested some of the funds of the rabbi in merchandise, bought at a low price and to be resold at a profit, using Joseph of Antioch as his agent. It so happened that just before he had, somewhat foolishly, handed over the charge of the treasury to Matthew he had bought some goods in this kind of speculation for which the payment was not complete. Joseph of Antioch, through his own agent, had agreed to pay the balance, and take what was still due out of the profit of the sale. But there had been no profit, for this particular shipment, bound for Caesarea, had been seized by the robber Barabbas. Judas had suffered a complete loss of the investment and was now being pressed to make up the balance owed. And now he had no funds.

Among the Jews it was not lawful to take a man to a civil court for nonpayment of debt. The matter was turned over to the Temple court, when the debt then became one owed to the Temple or to God. It was a great scandal in these circumstances if the payment was not made; and in the case of Judas, the scandal would descend on the rabbi, to the even greater mortification of Judas.

He was then at his wits' end how to repay Joseph of Antioch, and grumbled aloud when one of the sisters of Lazarus took a pound pot of precious ointment and anointed the feet of the rabbi with it. The ointment, which was of the purest nard, fragrant with the scent of wild rose, could have been better used, he said, if sold and the money given to the poor—though in fact he intended, had that been done, to keep back a portion to settle his debt with Joseph of Antioch.

The rabbi rebuked his murmurings, saying that the poor they would always have with them. "Let her be," he said, looking directly at Judas. "The ointment is for the day of my burial." It seemed to Judas that in these words there was a secret message for him—that he should cooperate in bringing about the death of the rabbi so that he could either demonstrate by resurrection that he was the Messiah or, remaining dead, put an end to the false beliefs of others including his own disciples.

Judas thought it no harm to inquire how much would be paid if he contrived to put the rabbi in the hands of Caiphas and the Sanhedrin and learned that he could expect thirty pieces of silver. This was precisely the amount he owed, and this seemed to him providential and tended to the conviction that to play the part of betrayer (for the very best of motives) was his appointed role. He therefore considered how he could do this.

CHAPTER TWENTY-FOUR

The celebration of the feast of the Passover among the Jews, combining a rejoicing over both a national and a religious liberation, was always an enormous problem to the Roman authorities in Palestine. Jews came from the remotest parts of the world for the feast, and the influx started weeks beforehand as caravans converged on Jerusalem from the farthest reaches of the empire. Some of these caravans were of tremendous size, containing four and five hundred camels with their attendant drivers and baggage. Roads were jammed. Rooms, unless bespoken several months ahead, were impossible to obtain. A city of tents arose around Jerusalem, in its extent twice the size of the city itself. The streets of the city were so packed that all camel and donkey traffic was forbidden. There was, indeed, scarcely room for pedestrians, who jammed the center of all the streets in a multicolored, slow-moving and countermoving stream, for the sides of the streets were occupied with stalls of merchandise of every description.

All the pilgrims of course gave offerings to the Temple, either purchased in Jerusalem or brought hundreds of miles on camel back. The offerings of gold, of silver, of sandalwood, of incense, of rich cloths, of scented oils and myrrh, of the feathers of ostriches, of ivory, and of ebony, and of frankincense—indeed of every kind of wealth—overflowed the Temple courtyards, awaiting purification before being deposited in the Temple treasury. These trains of wealth, converging upon the city, though heavily guarded by private armies of retainers, were a tempting prize for the brigands who infested the wilderness areas of Judaea.

A Roman preparation for the Passover, then, consisted in a roundup of all known brigands throughout the land. Some, thus seized, were crucified out of hand on the little hill outside of Jerusalem which was known as the Hill or Place of the Skulls. Pilate would have preferred to have distributed the crucifixions along the roads as providing a more widespread propaganda. But in this he was frustrated, as was so often the case, by Jewish scruples.

The Jews held as defiled any place where a man was executed. To have distributed the executions about the countryside, thus extending the defilement of land, would have promoted a riot, so all had to be done at the Place of the Skulls, which seemed to Pilate an atrocious and silly waste of punishment. He had then to content himself with two or three crucifixions a week on Golgotha, and since every man thus executed deprived him or Rome of a potential slave, he economized by ordering that those condemned were to be roped to the crosses rather than nailed. Crucified in this manner, the victims lasted much longer, some of them as much as eight days, though this seemed to depend more on weight than strength. A heavy man died faster. Golgotha, the place of execution, lay just beyond the city walls and close to the main road.

Among those seized in the roundup of brigands was

Barabbas. Pilate had not been anxious to seize Barabbas at this time. There was a rumor among the Jews that there was a connection between Pilate and Barabbas whereby in return for receiving a proportion of his loot, Pilate undertook to turn a blind eye on the activities of the brigand. But this was a libel on Pilate. He still suspected a connection between Barabbas and the rabbi from Nazareth; a well-concealed conspiracy of which John the Baptizer had been a part.

He wanted to give Barabbas more rope while he accumulated evidence, which was, however, not accumulating. His hand was forced in the matter of the arrest of Barabbas by the attack on the caravan of Joseph of Antioch. This had taken place on the road from the new city of Tiberias to Caesarea. Joseph of Antioch was too great a man for such an attack to go by unpunished. Pilate then ordered that Barabbas be hunted down. And so Barabbas had been found and arrested and was now in chains in the dungeons of the Antonia fortress at Jerusalem.

With the approach of the Passover, it was necessary to concentrate all available troops in Jerusalem, and Longinus had been ordered there with half of his command, leaving the post at Capernaum under an acting centurion. Longinus would have left the post under the command of Balba, except that Balba was too fond of wine to be trusted. So he had gone to Jerusalem with the senior centurion.

Immediately after the cure of his servant Ruafocus, Longinus had desired to do some good work to express his gratitude. He had approached the Pharisee, Simon, at Capernaum, asking whether he could make an offering to the god of the Jews but was told that nothing he offered could be put before their god, though he could obliquely make an offering in money which would be used, after purification, for the needs of the synagogue or the Temple. Later, however, when he had got all his money together for this purpose, it was to find this decision reversed. It appeared, on closer consultation, that his money, being that of a soldier, was blood money, and there was no purification in the world that would make it acceptable as either a synagogue or Temple offering.

Longinus, then, knowing that the rabbi had great compassion for the poor, took all the money he had and gave it to the poor, hoping that this would please the rabbi and be a sufficient offering of gratitude for the curing of his servant.

He was still puzzled about the nature of the rabbi. He had no doubts whatever about his powers. But he could not decide who he was, whether a god or a messenger of a god. The reports that came to him about the rabbi were widely conflicting. Some said he was a dealer in the black arts and that his power came from the devils of the Jewish religion. These devils, it seemed, had once been angels who had revolted against the Jewish god. They were enormously powerful, but not quite as powerful as the god of the Jews. But to those who turned to them, they gave some of their power, and this accounted for the miracles, he was told, he had seen performed by others who were not Jews and also for the miracles performed by the rabbi himself.

"He teaches against our religion and is therefore not a man of God but a man of demons," the people who held this view agreed. They supported their arguments with chapter and verse from their sacred writings. But others said of the rabbi that he was a great prophet; that he was the Messiah and would bring about the kingdom of the Jewish god on earth and that soon all would be converted to the Jewish faith and then a life of eternal joy and splendor would be granted to the whole earth. Those who resisted this conversion (they granted that some would) would perish horribly.

The centurion asked Bar Timeus, the disciple of the rabbi who had been cured of blindness, whether the rabbi was a god come to earth and if so what god.

"There is only one god, not many gods," said Bar Timeus.

"Then is the rabbi that god?" asked Longinus. But Bar Timeus could not answer beyond saying that the rabbi had been sent by the god of the Jews to lead them to salvation.

Ruafocus alone had no doubts about the nature of the rabbi. "He is God," he said. "The God the world has been waiting for."

"A god?" asked Longinus. "One of many?"

"No. The Supreme God," said Ruafocus. "My gods were conquered by yours. And now your gods are about to be conquered. Remember my dream of the wind blowing through the forests of my island? It was a dream that signified the coming of a new god, who would recreate everything and the rabbi is that god. He has made me young. I am going to live forever."

Ruafocus did not look any younger than when he had been snatched back from death at the bidding of the rabbi. His skin was still wrinkled, his arms thin and leathery. But his eyes were bright with a gaiety like those of a young boy, as if some treasure of happiness had been put before him which could not be taken away. He still suffered from cold and heat and pains in his bones, but these sufferings now bothered him no more than the tickling of a fly. His temper had improved, too, though he still delighted in needling the centurion.

"I suppose," he said when Longinus persisted in doubting that the rabbi was really a god, "that the first requirement to be a Roman is to be born a fool. There are certainly no people in the world as foolish as the Romans."

"What is your definition of a fool?" asked Longinus.

"Someone who believes nothing that cannot be proved. And then refuses to believe the proof when it is provided."

"You have proof that the rabbi is a god?" asked the centurion.

"The plainest proof which should be convincing to anyone but a Roman. Tell me, was it not acknowledged in Rome that the Emperor Augustus was a god and are not sacrifices offered before his statue?"

"Certainly," said Longinus.

"Did the Emperor Augustus ever cure lepers or people who were blind or dumb?"

"No."

"Did he ever raise a man from the dead?"

"No."

"So the rabbi who can do these things is obviously greater than the Emperor Augustus who is a god. Therefore the rabbi is a greater god than Augustus—or any of the gods you Romans sacrifice to."

"That is both impious and treasonous," warned the centurion.

"Nothing of the kind," said Ruafocus. "It is your view that it is treasonous and impious, and my view that it is truthful and devout. I am prepared to argue that case before Caesar himself or Pilate—since he is nearer."

"If you don't want any harm to come to yourself and the rabbi, you had better keep your mouth shut," said Longinus.

"Neither you nor Caesar nor all the legions of Rome could do any harm to the rabbi unless he willed it," said Ruafocus. "As for any harm coming to me, I have been born again. Indeed now that I look back, I realize that I was dead before but now I am truly alive, having been summoned into life by the rabbi. But you are still dead."

At these words the centurion recalled that John the Baptizer had told him that he was a dead man and had to be born again. He felt solitary and surrounded by darkness, and could find no comfort.

CHAPTER TWENTY-FIVE

After Lazarus had been raised from death, the rabbi stayed with him and his sisters Mary and Martha at Bethany, which was scarcely two miles from Jerusalem though separated from the city by a ridge of hills crowned by the Mount of Olives. The distance being so short, hundreds, even thousands, of those who had come to Jerusalem for the Passover came to Bethany to see the rabbi and also to see and speak with Lazarus.

This miracle produced a greater wonder among the people than any other the rabbi had performed, and the greater part of those who came to see him said openly that he was the Messiah and the Son of God. Nor were these any longer all the poorer sort—the Rejected. Among them were many rich men and members of both the Pharisees and the Sadducees. But these last were afraid to confess their belief openly, for they knew that if they did so they would then be cast out of the Temple and synagogues, and they could not bear such shame.

When the rabbi saw these priests believing in him but afraid to confess their belief, he became sad and spoke again of his own death to his disciples.

In the week before the Passover, he went to Jerusalem several times and preached in the Temple which had been erected in all its magnificence by Herod the Great. He went as soon as the gates had been flung open after the morning prayer, and crowds from all the nations of the world followed him into the courtyard to listen to him. There were far more about him, on these occasions, than about the other rabbis at the Temple or about Caiphas himself, and Caiphas was driven to distraction at the loss of all influence among the Jews. Yet he dared not move against the rabbi because of the multitude of his followers.

Peter was especially sensitive to the sorrow of the rabbi and sought to lift up his spirits by pointing out all the beauty and richness of the great Temple which was beyond any building in the world of that time in its treasure and elaboration. But the rabbi said to Peter, "The day will come in which there will not be left of this Temple one stone upon another which will not be thrown down."

Nor was he impressed when he saw huge loads of treasures being brought into the Temple as offerings, these great offerings being announced by blasts on a trumpet. But seeing a widow put two small coins in the offering box, he pointed her out to his disciples and said, "That poor woman has given more to God than all the treasure that has been brought here this day. For all these out of their abundance have given gifts to God; but she out of her want has put in all that she has to live on."

Peter, fearing for the safety of the rabbi since he knew of the enmity of Caiphas, was anxious that the Passover should be celebrated quietly at Bethany, but the rabbi told him, two days before the feast, to go to Jerusalem and reserve a room for them for the celebration.

"But, Rabbi," cried Peter, "to whom shall I go? Every place is already engaged."

"When you enter the city," said the rabbi, "you will see a man carrying a pitcher of water. Follow him into the house into which he goes. Say to the owner of the house, 'The Master says to you: where is the guest chamber that I may eat the Passover there with my disciples?' He will show you a large upper room, already furnished. Prepare the meal there."

Peter and John went as bidden, and everything occurred as the rabbi had said. They then arranged for the wine and the paschal lamb and the unleavened bread, which were the principal ingredients of the feast.

News that a room was being engaged for the rabbi in which to celebrate the Passover soon spread through the city. Hundreds flocked out of all the gates on the Bethany side to greet him as he came. They were in such multitudes that they completely lined the road from Bethany to Jerusalem, and they tore limbs from palm trees and from olive trees growing in the Mount of Olives and put these before him, crying out, "Blessed is he who comes in the name of the Lord, the king of Israel."

The multitude was so thick that the rabbi could hardly move forward, and because there were so many who could not see him, particularly women and children who were pressed to the back to the crowd, he mounted himself on a young donkey and so came on toward Jerusalem on a road which was made for him of palm branches and olive branches and handfuls of wild spring flowers plucked from the hillsides and indeed the very robes of the people.

Before entering the city gates he turned to the people and said, "The hour has come for the Son of Man to be glorified. Unless the grain of wheat falls into the ground and dies it remains lone. But if it dies, it brings forth much fruit. He who loves his life, loses it; and he who hates his life in this world, keeps it until life everlasting.

"If anyone serves me, let him follow me; and where I am there also shall my servant be. If anyone serves me, my Father will honor him." For a little while after he had said this, he fell silent and he seemed to be in an agony of mind for he exclaimed aloud, "Now my soul is troubled. And what shall I say? Father, save me from this hour? No. This is why I came to this hour. I will say rather: Father, glorify your name."

Immediately he had said this a great wind swept over the people, rustling the trees and tearing at their garments like a gale. The air was filled with dust and twigs and leaves, and the wind hissed and moaned about them. Then the wind dropped, the air was perfectly still and a voice was heard by some saying, "I have both glorified my name, and I will glorify it again." Many heard the words distinctly, but others heard only a sound and believed that the windstorm had been followed by a roll of thunder.

The news that the rabbi was to come to Jerusalem for the Passover was soon known to the Roman authorities also, and when the crowds started to stream through the gates to greet him, some soldiers were sent to see that no riot occurred. These were led by Longinus, the centurion with authority in Galilee. He could not get to the rabbi himself without riding down the crowd, but he saw Philip, one of the rabbi's disciples, and shouted to him to come over.

"Ask the rabbi if I may speak with him privately," said the centurion. But Philip himself, because of the press of the crowd, could not get to the rabbi, so he called out the message to Andrew, who was closer to him. Andrew, respecting the centurion, passed the message to the rabbi. But the rabbi only looked at the centurion and said nothing.

It was now close to sunset and the crowd dissolved, for the hour of the beginning of the Passover was at hand and all needed to go to their own homes to make their preparations. The rabbi then was able to enter the city and go to the room that Peter and John had prepared.

When they were all together and he had seated them at the table he said, "I have greatly desired to eat this Passover with you before I suffer, for I say to you that I will eat no more until it has been fulfilled in the Kingdom of Heaven." But they did not understand what he meant. Nor did they immediately understand what followed, for the rabbi, taking water and a towel, bade them all be seated. Then he went from one to the other, washing their feet. But when he came to Peter, Peter said what had been in the minds of them all, "Lord, you would wash my feet?"

"What I do, you don't understand now," said the rabbi. "But you will understand it later."

As the rabbi bent to the floor for the washing, kneeling before Peter, Peter was overcome with shame and said, "Lord, I will never allow you to wash my feet." The rabbi looked up at him and shook his head. "The rock, I called you, Peter," he said. "And hard you are of understanding. If I do not wash your feet, Peter, you will have no part with me."

"Then, Lord," said Peter, "wash not only my feet but my hands also and my head so that I may be wholly part of you."

The rabbi replied, "He who has already bathed needs

only to wash his feet after a journey and he is clean all over. And you, my disciples, are clean, but not all of you." When he said that he looked at Judas.

Then he put aside the water and the towel and explained to them that he had washed their feet as an example to them. If he who was their master would kneel and wash their feet then they ought to do the same for each other, no man holding himself too lofty for such a task. All understood the rebuke, for there had been arguments among the disciples as to which of them stood highest in the regard of the rabbi.

The four cups of wine were then drunk to start the meal and then the unleavened bread was put before the rabbi and he broke it and gave a piece to each one, saying to them, "This is my body, which is being given for you; do this in remembrance of me." He also took the cup of wine before him and said, "This cup is the new covenant of my blood, which shall be shed for you. And behold the hand of him who is to betray me is with me on the table."

But the hands of many of the disciples were on the table at that moment, including those of Peter and John, who was seated next to the rabbi and was resting his head against his shoulder in love. So they all asked, "Lord, who is to betray you? Is it I?" They were in a hubbub over the matter, pressing him for answers and assuring each other that they would not countenance such a thing.

Only John, then, heard the rabbi say, "He to whom I shall dip the 'bread' and give it. He will betray me." He then took some of the unleavened bread, dipped it in the gravy of the roast lamb and gave it to Judas of Kerioth. Judas stared at the rabbi, seemingly paralyzed, and the rabbi said to him, "What you do, do quickly."

Amazed that the rabbi should know what had been so

long in his mind, and convincing himself that the words of the rabbi were a confirmation of the role which he had convinced himself he was to play, Judas immediately left. The others seeing him go did not suspect anything, for they were still concerned about the prophecy of betrayal and their own loyalty. The rabbi silenced them and said, "My children, yet a while I am with you. Then I will be gone. You will seek me and where I go you cannot come. I give you a new commandment. Love one another. As I have loved you, so you also love one another. By this, all men will know that you are my disciples, if you have love for one another."

Peter, heavy with fear, said, "Lord, where are you going?"

The rabbi repeated, "Where I am going, you cannot follow me. But you will follow me later."

Peter said, "Why can I not follow you? I will follow you anywhere. I will lay down my life for you."

The rabbi shook his head and said, "Will you indeed lay down your life for me, Peter? I assure you that the cock will not crow tomorrow morning before you have denied me three times." And at this Peter burst into tears because he could find no way to make the rabbi believe in his love and loyalty.

CHAPTER TWENTY-SIX

When Judas had left the rabbi and the other disciples, he went immediately to the house of Caiphas the high priest to tell him where the rabbi could be found alone, so that he could be arrested and Judas could receive the promised award of thirty pieces of silver which he owed to Joseph of Antioch.

Caiphas was keeping the feast of the Passover with all his household, and Judas had great difficulty in obtaining an answer to his knocking on the great door that gave entrance to the high priest's gardens with the dwelling beyond. Even the watchman had left his post for the Passover, but eventually a gatekeeper came and, opening the door scarcely more than a few inches, hissed at Judas to be gone and not disturb the Passover of the high priest.

But Judas told the porter that he must be taken immediately to the high priest for he had important news concerning the rabbi of Nazareth. Even so, he was made to wait outside, during which doubts concerning his actions crowded his mind so that he was almost on the point of running away when the door was again opened, and this time he was conducted to Caiphas. He found Caiphas alone, in a small chamber to the side of his dining room.

"What have you to say to me at such a time?" demanded Caiphas.

"Rabbi," said Judas, "I am one of the disciples of the rabbi of Nazareth. I am prepared to deliver him into your hands tonight in return for the reward which has been offered."

"You fool," said Caiphas. "What can we do with him now with Jerusalem full of his followers? If we lay a finger on him, he has but to call out and there will be such a riot that we ourselves will be slain. This is not the time to move against him."

"But he will not resist or call out," said Judas. "He expects to be turned over to the Sanhedrin and put to death. He has told us so. He says the time for this to happen is now at hand. It is because of this that I have come to you—to fulfill that which he prophesied about himself."

"What else has he prophesied in this matter?" asked Caiphas, eying Judas closely.

"That on the third day he will rise again from the dead," said Judas.

"He has said this?" asked Caiphas.

"Yes," said Judas. "Some thought he spoke of the Temple, but he spoke of himself. So he has explained it privately to us, his disciples."

"Do you believe him?" asked Caiphas.

"I do not know," said Judas. "I saw him raise Lazarus, but I do not know whether he can raise himself."

"Lazarus was not dead," said Caiphas. "He was only drugged. If your rabbi is crucified, don't look for his resurrection, for we will make sure he is dead." He turned from Judas deep in thought. Here was an opportunity to seize the rabbi which might not come soon again. But it was the worst of possible times, because of the thousands of his supporters that thronged Jerusalem. Yet, thinking further, Caiphas decided that if the rabbi could be seized that night, when all Jews were in their homes observing the Passover, the matter might be kept secret from them and a riot avoided.

The following day was the eve of the Great Sabbath of the Passover, when everybody would be busy with a multitude of tasks so that no work would require to be done on the Sabbath itself. Even the household supply of water would have been laid in on the morrow before the Sabbath. During the next twenty-four hours then the people would be extremely busy. If the rabbi, seized that very night, could be quickly tried and executed on the eve of the Great Sabbath, his supporters might not hear of it until the business was done. Boldness could bring the matter to a successful conclusion, and Caiphas was a young enough man to act boldly.

"Where may this man be found?" he asked.

"Sir," said Judas, "he keeps the Passover at present with eleven other of his disciples. But it is his habit to visit the Mount of Olives to meditate and pray whenever he is in Jerusalem and I know that he will go there soon. He goes there because as you know the place is always deserted at night. He may be taken there and he will have none with him but eleven of his followers."

"It will be dark," said Caiphas. "How is he to be recognized? He may escape. All look alike in darkness."

"I will identify him," said Judas. "He to whom I give the kiss of peace will be the rabbi."

There was a small table in the corner of the outer chamber, which was otherwise empty of furniture, with a gong on it. Caiphas went to the table and struck the gong and a Levite appeared from the adjoining room.

"Summon a cohort of the Temple guard, equipped with

torches and weapons, and have them go with this man," he said. "Then immediately send messengers to those of the Sanhedrin who are of my mind in the matter of the rabbi of Nazareth to meet me here. Tell them they are bid by myself to assemble here. Also bring any of the Levites and Temple servants who have heard the rabbi preach in the Temple so we may have witnesses against him."

"And the money?" asked Judas.

"Give this man thirty pieces of silver on his return with the rabbi," said Caiphas.

"He is to be brought immediately to your house?" asked Judas.

Caiphas thought for a moment and then said, "No. Take him first to the house of Annas. He must have a hand in this matter as well as I. It must appear that we act together."

The rabbi had gone, as Judas said, after the Supper, to the Mount of Olives to pray and meditate, taking the disciples with him. He told them to stay in one place while he went to pray by himself, but that they should pray also. But Peter found that he was incapable of prayer. Distraught over the rabbi's prophecy that he, Peter, would betray the rabbi that every night, his mind was wearied and in this weariness Peter fell asleep and the others also. He was awakened by the rabbi, who chided him on his sleeping.

"Could you not watch one short hour with me?" he said to Peter. "Watch and pray that you may not enter into temptation."

"I will, Lord," said Peter. "I will."

The rabbi shook his head sorrowfully and said, "The spirit indeed is willing, but the flesh is weak." He went away again to pray and when he returned, he found Peter again asleep. He left him then and went to pray once more. When he returned he shook Peter and said, "Rise. Let us go. Behold, he who betrays me is at hand."

At the mention of betrayal Peter was immediately awake, for his mind was still busy with the rabbi's statement that he, Peter, would deny him that very night. He had become confused about this statement and the prophecy that one of them would betray him, and he was filled with apprehension that, even against his own will, he would be trapped into a betrayal of the rabbi, for he knew nothing of the actions or thoughts of Judas.

He had brought with him a sword as an earnest of his pledge that he would protect the rabbi even to death, and he grasped it now, and heard, as he stood, a chattering of voices in the dark. Then several lights of torches appeared, bobbing here and there in the blackness, and he ran to the side of the rabbi and drew the sword.

What happened next took him completely by surprise. He saw in the torchlight a group of Temple soldiers coming towards the rabbi led by Judas. Peter recognized Judas and concluded that, summoned by Judas, who shared Peter's concern for the rabbi's safety, the soldiers had come to protect him.

When the soldiers were about twenty feet off, the rabbi called out, "Whom are you seeking?" They had not seen him, for the torchlight did not penetrate that far.

The group stopped immediately, not a man moving, and one called out, "Jesus, the Rabbi of Nazareth."

"I am he," said the rabbi. But instead of coming toward him, they looked uncertainly at each other.

"Come," said the rabbi. "I am he whom you seek." But still they did not move.

Then Judas came forward with the Levite Malchus,

who was the secretary of the high priest, and two or three others who were bolder. Judas went to the rabbi and said, "Hail, Rabbi," and kissed him on the cheek.

"Friend," said the rabbi gently, "for what purpose have you come?"

Judas stared at him, his eyes filled with fear and doubt, and said, "Rabbi, you do not know?"

Immediately Malchus and one of the soldiers seized the rabbi and Peter, brought to his senses by this action, gave a shout and struck at the head of Malchus with his sword. Malchus dodged the blow, moving back and pulling his head aside, but the point of Peter's sword lopped off his right ear, which hung dangling by a piece of the lobe on his shoulder, and a blossom of blood bloomed suddenly on the side of his head.

"Put up your sword, Peter," cried the rabbi. "I caution you that all who take the sword will perish by the sword. Peter! Peter! Do you not even now know that I have but to ask my Father and he will send me at this moment ten legions of angels to deliver me? But how, if this were done, could the Scriptures be fulfilled that prophesied that this must take place?"

Malchus had fallen back and was holding his hand to his ear, filled with fright over the injury done to him but so stunned he could not make a sound. Blood trickled between his fingers and down the sleeve of his robe. The rabbi turned to him and said, "Malchus, see I heal you, for you were wrongly injured." He then put his hand over the bloodied hand of Malchus and his ear was immediately restored. When Judas saw this, he fled into the darkness.

The soldiers were now at a loss what to do, but, fearing the high priest to whom they were subject and who could punish them with scourging if they disobeyed his orders, they came to the rabbi and surrounded him, and he, without the slightest opposition, followed them out of the garden. Malchus went with them, hoping that no harm would now come to the rabbi when he told Caiphas of how he had healed his ear.

The other disciples hung in the background, outside the group of soldiers, confused about what was going on. Peter was among them. He knew the rabbi was being arrested but since the rabbi had rebuked him for using his sword, he did not know what to do further.

But John pushed his way through the guard of soldiers to walk beside the rabbi and took his hand in his and in this manner they walked together to the house of Annas, the other high priest. When they got there, all the other disciples had left except John and Peter.

Annas had already been warned by Caiphas to expect the rabbi, but Annas did not question him in his house, which had been purified, but in the courtyard and by the light of torches. The gate was shut during the questioning, and Peter remained outside though John entered with the rabbi. When John saw that Peter had been shut out, he went to the woman who guarded the gate and told her to let Peter in, since he was one of the disciples of the rabbi, and so he was admitted. Unlike John, he did not stand in the forefront with the soldiers, but remained far away in the shadows by the gate.

Annas then questioned the rabbi. "I have heard," he said, "that you preach blasphemy and denounce the teachings of Moses and of Abraham. You mock at purification and at sacrifices made in the Temple and bring our religion into disrepute. What do you say to that?"

The rabbi replied, "Annas, why do you not question

those who have heard me preach? Ask them what I have said. I have spoken openly in the Temple and in the synagogues before many people. Question those who heard me. Or do you not know the law concerning witnesses?"

At this, one of the Levites struck the rabbi in the face and said, "Is that the way you answer the high priest?"

The rabbi looked at him mildly and replied, "If I have spoken a blasphemy then you yourself can bear witness against me. But if I have not, for what reason do you strike me?" Then he said to Annas, "Can this man, on what I have said here, provide you with a witness against me?"

Annas was at a loss what to do, for he had been confronted with a situation manufactured by Caiphas and with which he himself did not agree. "Take him to Caiphas," he said. "This is his business." Then he withdrew into his house.

While this had been going on, Peter had remained at the gate where there was a brazier. He felt as if he were dying of cold and yet could not seem to get any warmth from the fire, though he stood close to it. The woman who tended the gate and other servants were around, and she said to Peter, "Are you not one of that man's disciples?"

"Me?" cried Peter. "No. I am not."

"Surely you are one of them," the woman persisted.

"You are mistaken," said Peter. "You are thinking of another man."

The rabbi was then taken before Caiphas, who had called together the members of the Lesser Sanhedrin who agreed with his views. Among these were many of the Pharisees, scribes and Levites, but none of the Sadducees were present at this tribunal which was of the Pharisee party whom Caiphas sought to court. Caiphas had also got together a number of witnesses against the rabbi, mostly from the Temple workers who were subject to his authority. He called on them one by one to repeat what they had heard the rabbi preach in the Temple.

Some said they had heard him say he could destroy the Temple in three days and build it again. Others said that he had claimed to be the Messiah and that he was greater than Elias, and that he had been born before Abraham, who had now been dead for several hundred years. But these charges were not enough, and no witnesses with more serious charges could be found. Furthermore the rabbi said not a word in his defense, and at last Caiphas, losing patience with both the witnesses and the rabbi, jumped up from his seat and shouted at him, "Haven't you got anything to say about the charges that are made against you by all these people?"

Still the rabbi made no reply and Caiphas, pointing his finger at the rabbi, cried, "I call on you to say, in the name of God, whether you are the Holy One, the son of God."

Abjured in the name of God to answer, even though by Caiphas, the rabbi said, "You have spoken the truth. Hereafter you will see the Son of Man sitting at the right hand of God and coming upon the clouds of Heaven."

Caiphas stared, white-faced, for a moment, at the rabbi, stunned by this announcement. Then, seizing his own outer robe, he tore it apart and cried to the others, "He has blasphemed before us all. What further need have we of witnesses? You have heard the blasphemy yourself. What is your verdict?"

"Death," they cried, and they started shouting at the rabbi, throwing aside in their jubilation and hate the dignity of the meeting. Some even spat at him, and others rushed from their seats to slap his face and demand that he prophesy who struck him. Caiphas himself seized the rabbi by the beard and spat in his face for it was necessary that he show himself even more vehement in the denunciation of blasphemy than the rest.

"Take him to Pilate," he said. "And let us demand that he be crucified."

Now Malchus, the Levite, who was secretary to Caiphas, had been hoping to be called as a witness so that he would tell how his ear had first been struck off by Peter and then restored by the rabbi. To support the truth of his story he looked about for Peter so that Peter could testify that he had cut off his ear. Malchus learned that Peter was in the courtyard and went to him and said, "You are the one who cut off my ear with your sword. Come now with me to Caiphas to testify."

But Peter looked at him wild-eyed with fear and said, "What are you talking about? Are you mad? I know nothing of the rabbi or of your ear." Immediately he said this the cock crowed and Peter tore himself away from Malchus and rushed into the streets, weeping. And from that day forward he never heard the cock crow without tears.

CHAPTER TWENTY-SEVEN

The cock crow that marked Peter's third denial of the rabbi, followed by a strident chorus of crowing from every quarter of the city, woke Pilate and his household at the praetorium.

Pilate kept his visits to Jerusalem to the minimum, for he found that when there he was besieged with petitions and delegations from one sect or another of the Jews, all insistent that their particular business had to come ahead of that of anyone else.

He had, however, of necessity to come to Jerusalem for the week of the Passover because of the concentration of his subjects in that city and the resultant concentration of the soldiers under his command in the Antonia fortress and other camps erected outside the city walls to accommodate them. Two full legions were needed to keep the turbulent Jews in order during the feast, and he had hardly finished with his toilet on arising, and eaten his usual light meal of the day, before he was informed that a delegation of the Jews, led by Caiphas, was waiting on him and insistent that they be given audience right away.

On any other occasion, he would have kept them cooling their heels several hours or perhaps even days before receiving them. But the national fervor which marked the Feast of the Passover made this the wrong time to slight the high priest, lest a riot be incited.

Pilate realized also that the high priest, on the first day of the Passover, would not be coming to see him unless it was on a matter of grave importance. So he told his secretary that he would receive Caiphas immediately, only to be reminded that Caiphas could not enter the praetorium because he would be defiled, so the interview would have to take place in the grounds of the palace.

This insult to Rome—that he was unclean and would defile the Jewish priest—added to Pilate's mounting anger, and he said he would see the high priest on the terrace of the praetorium overlooking the quadrangle which was used for the drilling and assembly of troops. Since this area could be entered without entering the praetorium proper, Caiphas and the members of the Sanhedrin were agreeable, after some hesitation, to meeting him there.

The business they had surprised Pilate only for a moment. Caiphas wanted him to condemn to crucifixion the rabbi of Nazareth whom they thrust before him bound—the same rabbi of Nazareth whom he had at one time suspected of leading a secret organization directed against Rome.

He was surprised only at the suddenness of the demand, for he knew that something of the sort was likely to develop because of the emnity of the Pharisees and the High Priest Caiphas to the rabbi. This emnity, of course, completely suited his purpose of dividing the Jews, and he was by no means ready to condemn the rabbi to death and so deprive himself of a useful tool of government.

"What charge do you bring against this man?" he asked.

"He is perverting the whole nation," said Caiphas. "He has forbidden the payment of taxes to Caesar and he says that he is the Messiah and therefore the king of the Jews."

The charges were vehement but general and Caiphas asked the rabbi, "Are you the king of the Jews?"

He asked the question in Latin and the rabbi made no reply. Thinking he could not understand the language, Pilate put the question again in Aramaic, for he had been long enough in Judaea to be familiar with the language. The reply he received was, "You say it," and Pilate knew enough of Aramaic idiom to realize that this was no reply at all. It was neither an affirmation nor a denial but a subtle suggestion that the questioner himself might, by his own investigation, discover the answer.

"Have you forbidden the payment of taxes to Caesar?" he asked.

Again the rabbi made no reply. But John, who was still with the rabbi, shouted, "He has told us to render to Caesar the things that are Caesar's and to God the things that are God's. And in this lies his fault." John was cuffed by one of the Temple guards that had accompanied Caiphas, but Pilate commanded them to leave the man alone.

"You bring general charges against this man and nothing specific," said Pilate. "You demand his death and you are all his accusers. But where are your witnesses? And what is your hurry in this matter? If the man is guilty let him be properly tried and at leisure. I suspect that you do not want judgment of me but condemnation of the man out of hand and that I will not give you."

"But he is stirring up all the people against Rome," cried Caiphas. "He is spreading sedition all the way from Galilee, even here to Jerusalem."

"Is he then from Galilee?" asked Pilate, though he well knew that this was so.

"Yes, from Nazareth."

Pilate saw immediately an escape for himself and an embarrassment for Herod. "Take him then to the Tetrarch Herod," he said. "He is not subject to my immediate jurisdiction."

And so the rabbi was led before Herod Antipas, who was also in Jerusalem for the Passover. He was a vain enough man to be pleased that Pilate had sent the rabbi to him, openly acknowledging his authority. And he was also pleased to meet the rabbi of whose miracles he had received many reports.

"Come," said Herod, "work a miracle before me and your accusers and you will immediately be set free and with honor."

But the rabbi held his peace and made no move. The same accusations were brought against him with the demand that he be put to death. But Herod had the cunning of a fox. He was already hated because of the beheading of John the Baptizer and he was not going to add to the hatred of the people by ordering the execution of a man who he knew had an enormous following among the country people of the land. On the other hand, he could not afford the animosity of the high priest, the scribes and the Pharisees who indeed had no great love for him. So to placate them he turned to the guard and said, "This man says he is your king, and that I am not. Let me see what kind of homage you are prepared to pay him."

The soldiers looked at one another nonplussed, and

then a senior among them said, "Why, tribute is due to a king and let me be the first to pay it." Then he struck the rabbi such a blow in the face as to knock him down. He was immediately picked up by the others, but only to be knocked down again, so that in Herod's presence, the rabbi was beaten about the floor with blows to the face, the stomach, the neck and the groin, all delivered as tribute from the soldiers to the new king. Then Herod threw a purple robe to the soldiers and said, "Put that on him so that Pilate may see how I honor this new king of the Jews. And take him back to Pilate. I happily surrender to him authority over this new ruler."

The rabbi then was led back to Pilate through a secret way that communicated between Herod's palace and the praetorium, so that if any were about in the streets, he would not be seen. In the interval Pilate's wife, Procula, having heard that the rabbi had been brought to trial, came to Pilate and told him to have nothing to do with the matter.

Her podgy, freckled face was pink with anxiety and she said, "I dreamed that some evil will befall us if any harm is done to this just man."

"Woman," said Pilate, "I cannot rule subject to your dreams and soothsayers. It does not serve my own purposes to have him killed, if that will comfort you. In any case I have sent him to Herod, thereby gaining credit and avoiding responsibility."

He was disconcerted then to have the rabbi brought back to him by Herod, but noted with sour admiration how nicely Herod had got out of the situation by turning the only serious charge against the rabbi, that of being king of the Jews, into a mock. He wished he had thought of that device himself.

Again the charges were repeated, with even more insistent demands that he order the rabbi crucified, and Pilate searched for an escape.

He was beginning now to feel a little sympathy for the rabbi, though that was foreign to his nature. The rabbi's face was bruised and swollen, his lips pulped, his nose running with blood. Yet he did not whimper or grovel, or even make any attempt to defend himself against his accusers, and Pilate became curious about his attitude. He therefore ordered him to be brought into the praetorium to be questioned, away from the high priest and the others who could not themselves enter the building.

Again he put the question to the rabbi, "Are you the king of the Jews?"

This time the rabbi answered him though with another question. "Do you say this of your own knowledge, or have others told you about me?" he asked.

"Am I a Jew?" demanded Pilate angrily. "Your own people have made the accusation to me. What have you done? Have you claimed to be their king?"

The rabbi replied, "I am indeed a king, but my kingdom is not of this world. If my kingdom were of this world, my followers would have fought that I might not be delivered to the high priest and the Pharisees. But as you see my kingdom is not such as yours."

"But you are some kind of king—in your own mind," said Pilate.

"That is so," said the rabbi. "I am a king. And that is why I have been born and have come into this world, to bear witness to the truth. Everyone who searches for the truth hears my voice."

"What is truth?" said Pilate with contempt. "It does not exist. It is what men make of it. You say that is why you have come into this world. What do you mean by that? Where are you from? Are you not just born like any other man?"

But to this the rabbi made no reply and Pilate became angry with him. "You fool," he said. "Why don't you answer me? Don't you know that I have power to crucify you or to set you free?"

"You would have no power over me at all," said the rabbi, "were it not given to you by God."

"I will show you what power I have," said Pilate angrily, "and then perhaps you will talk differently." He then turned to the guard and said, "Take this man and scourge him. Lay on hard and loosen his tongue and lower his pride."

For the first time since his arrest, Roman troops now took custody of the rabbi. They were of course Syrians, with a great hatred of the Jews and were subject to the scourge themselves.

Two of them had indeed been scourged the previous day for alleged insults to the Jews and, having now a Jew in their hands with orders to scourge him, they relished the opportunity. They took him to an armory which was also the place of military punishment and strapped him by the hands to a small post so that his back would be well arched and the spine exposed. Of course, he would not stand very long. The first blow or two with the nine-tongued scourge, to which were fastened pieces of metal, would knock him to the ground. But his arms being tied, and his clothing stripped off him, his whole body then would be exposed to the blows.

The men were experts in the punishment and liked the low post which gave a bigger range for their swing, and they made the thongs whistle through the air as they brought them down on the back of the rabbi.

There were a dozen men called for the sport and they

smiled to see the Jew's muscles knotting under the lashes, the flesh crawling and trembling and the dead white lines across the torso become, a second later, crimson stripes as they filled with blood. They spared no part of the man, letting the lash curl around flanks and belly and buttocks until they were satisfied.

Then, having been told that he claimed to be a king of the Jews, they sat him on a stool and hailed him as king, butting him with their fists and spitting on him. Tiring of this, they took him out to Pilate again, the purple cloak around him and his feet and hands dripping with blood that flowed down them from his torso, legs and arms.

Pilate thought that such a sight might satisfy Caiphas and the Sanhedrin. These had been waiting in the quadrangle during the scourging, but had been joined by Temple servants who had been summoned by Caiphas. When the rabbi was brought out, after the scourging, he was almost unrecognizable. The scourgers had not spared even his face with the lash, and his long hair and beard, once fair, were now dark and greasy with blood. His whole body shook violently beneath the purple robe and yet he was able to stand upright and did not fall to his knees, groveling for pity.

With a gesture, Pilate told the soldiers to bring the man up to him on the terrace. He then himself flung off the purple robe so that Caiphas and the others could see the lacerated body. Some drew back with a sharp intake of breath at the sight.

"Behold the man," said Pilate, pointing to the rabbi's torn body. "What more would you have me to do with him!"

Immediately there was a cry, "Crucify him! Crucify him!"

But the Pilate was still unwilling to do so, and he sent to the dungeons for Barabbas, who had also been condemned to death. It was the custom that when two men were thus condemned during the Passover, one could be released by acclamation. So Barabbas was brought and also stripped and stood before them, and when Pilate looked at the two, he was shocked, for between Barabbas and the rabbi, bloodied as he was, there was a marked similarity of appearance. Barabbas, long confined in the dungeon, was blinded in the sunlight and Pilate asked him, "Is not this man your brother?"

"I do not know him," said Barabbas. "Who is he?"

"You have heard of him surely," said Pilate. "He is the rabbi from Nazareth."

Then Barabbas remembered that he had been mistaken for the rabbi once before and grinned. "He owes me a favor," he said. "Perhaps I will be lucky today."

Pilate now turned to the crowd and said, "Whom of these two shall I set free according to your custom?"

They shouted, "Barabbas."

"And what shall I do with this other man?" Pilate demanded.

"Crucify him," they shouted.

"But I find no harm in him," said Pilate.

"He says he is king of the Jews and if you do not crucify him, you are no friend of Caesar's" replied Caiphas. The implied threat in those words shook Pilate, for his whole position depended on not losing one scruple of the favor of Tiberius.

"Take him then," he said. "And do what you want with him. But for me, I find him innocent and I wash my hands of his death."

"Let his death be on us," cried Caiphas.

Pilate then called to his secretary to make out the order for execution to be brought to him for signature. And while the order was being drawn up, his mind, always busy with such matters, considered the political implications of the execution.

Since he had been outmaneuvered in the matter of putting the rabbi to death he considered whether there was not yet a way to extract some kind of advantage for himself over Caiphas and over the Jews as a whole who had had their way.

When his secretary brought him the order of execution to sign he said, "Make out a superscription in Latin, Greek and Aramaic, stating the crime for which this man is crucified," he said. "Let it read: 'The king of the Jews.' "

Caiphas, who was standing close by, heard this and said, "Excellency. The superscription should read: 'He says he is the king of the Jews.' "

Pilate looked at him coldly. "It is your crucifixion, my superscription," he said. "It shall stand as: 'The king of the Jews.' In this matter, my dear Caiphas, I look to your own interests, for surely Caesar will be the more impressed by your love for him if in his name you have crucified your own king."

He searched for one further detail concerning the execution which, since it had to be carried out, would be of benefit to him. He had received a report from his agents that the senior centurion at Capernaum had so far forgotten the dignity of his position as a Roman officer as to go to this rabbi in full uniform in the presence of a multitude of the Jews and beg some favor of him concerning his servant. This loss of prestige had to be made good and at the same time the loyalty of the centurion, who seemed to favor the Jews overmuch, tested. So when he had signed the order, he gave it to a guard and said, "Take this to the Antonia and inform the tribune that this crucifixion is to be carried out by Longinus, the senior centurion at Capernaum, and by no other."

CHAPTER TWENTY-EIGHT

"Ah," said Gaius Servius, the tribune to whom Longinus was immediately responsible, "Fortune has smiled on you today, Centurion. While others stand guard over that noisy and vulgar rabble of the Jews—have you ever noticed how they smell, Centurion; something sour, akin to starving horses?—you are to preside at a public entertainment."

Longinus said nothing, but, knowing the tribune's taste in entertainments, he was apprehensive.

"A spectacle of death," said the tribune. "Quite the most dramatic entertainment that life offers—and indeed its culmination. I am devoted to death, you know. It is exquisite in its mystery. Far superior to birth. Of course, if one can witness the two together—birth and death—then that is all that life offers in pleasure and excitement. I recall a slave girl of mine, that Canaanite girl you may remember at the baths in Caesarea. Well, at my command, she was brought to me at the time of the birth of her child so that I might watch. And she obliged me, the dear girl, in dying the moment the child was born. It was tremendous. Such devotion to her master. Really I weep for her."

Still the centurion said nothing and the tribune studied him for a moment and said, "Really, what a dull man you are. If Pilate himself had not ordered it I would give this duty to another whom I could rely on returning to me with all the interesting details. Here are your orders," and he pushed two pieces of parchment across the table to the centurion.

Longinus picked them up and read on the first, written in three languages, the words, "The king of the Jews." He turned to the second, the order for execution, and read it through in disbelief.

"It is Pilate's instruction that you supervise the crucifixion yourself," said the tribune.

The centurion stared at him in shock, incapable of a move, for his mind seemed to have utterly gone from him and he had no command over himself.

"On your way, Centurion," said the tribune. "Attend to your orders."

"Sir," said the centurion, recovering himself, "is it permitted for me to see Pilate about this?"

"For what purpose?" demanded the tribune.

"I cannot do it," said Longinus. "I must beg him to assign the duty to another."

"See Pilate if you wish," said the tribune. "I always suspected that your liver was white and your heart Jewish."

But Longinus paid no attention to this and went immediately to Pilate and gained admission as soon as he arrived, for Pilate had been expecting some such development.

"Excellency," said the centurion, "I have served over thirty years with the legions and have many decorations as proof of my bravery and my loyalty and devotion to

Rome. I have never disobeyed an order nor hung back when an attack was commanded. But I ask you to relieve me of this duty. Let it be done by another."

"Longinus," said Pilate, "I am well aware of your long service to Rome. It is admirable. It has commanded the respect of all your previous generals and it commands mine too. Yet each of us must, however long our service, be prepared at any moment to demonstrate our loyalty anew, without reliance on what is past.

"Tell me, if I ordered you to lay down your life for Rome at this instant, would you hesitate, Centurion?"

"I would not," replied Longinus.

"Then for Rome, I order you to crucify this man," said Pilate. "You and no other. And that because you unthinkingly, as I choose to believe, brought a slight upon Rome by going to him at one time in your full uniform, with all the badges of your office, and begging him, a Jew, for some service connected with your private servant. Rome does not beg, particularly of the Jews. Therefore wipe out this slight on your country and on your comrades, and take him and crucify him."

"You order it, Excellency?" asked the centurion.

"I order it," said Pilate. The look on the centurion's face moved Pilate and he said, more gently, "Come, Centurion. Consider all the years of your loyal service now in the balance. Consider that the man must be crucified, in any case. You have not brought about his death. You are only the instrument of it. If you have some attachment to this rabbi, it must not interfere with your duty as a soldier. But you may ask yourself privately whether it is dishonorable to assist a friend into death who must die anyway. You may find, without violating the letter of the sentence, methods of speeding his end and shortening his agony, which others might not think of."

When the centurion made no comment on this, he said sharply, "Well, Centurion, do you obey your orders?"

"I obey them, Excellency, though I destroy myself," said Longinus.

"That has always been expected of a soldier of Rome," said Pilate dryly, and dismissed him.

When he got back to the Antonia, Longinus told Balba of the order to execute the rabbi and Balba stared at him for a moment and then laughed. "For Rome nothing is impossible," he said. "We put to death those who raise the dead. This will make us famous. When I tell the story in my old age it will be good at any time for a free cup of wine. How many men, Centurion?"

"Yourself and three others," said Longinus. The men were brought and Longinus went with them to the guard-room of the Antonia to take charge of the rabbi. He found him seated on a stone bench, so bloodied from the scourging that the blood stained both the bench and the floor below him. There were several other soldiers present, all trying to avoid looking at the rabbi, for it was bad luck to speak to or be recognized by a man condemned to death.

Longinus, being the senior officer present, cleared the guardroom of all but himself, Balba and the rabbi. When they were alone he stood before the rabbi, whose head was bowed, and said, "Rabbi, you have been ordered to be crucified, and I am he who must carry out this order."

The rabbi raised his head to look at him, but said nothing, and Longinus thought for a moment that he did not recognize him.

"Rabbi," he said, "I am that Roman officer of Capernaum whose servant, Ruafocus, you brought back from death."

Still the rabbi said nothing, only looking at him.

"Rabbi," said the centurion, "I do not know what manner of person you are except that you are a good man and innocent. Forgive me, Rabbi, that it is my fate to crucify you who cured my servant."

Then for the first time the rabbi spoke saying, "Centurion, you commit no fault and you need no forgiveness. Do that which you have been ordered to do."

There was still some delay for a cross had to be brought from the armorer's storeroom where these things were kept, and Balba, sent for it, came back with the tau cross, so called, because it was shaped like the Greek letter. He brought only the crossbeam of this gallows, with a mortise already cut through the center, for the uprights were always kept erected on the Hill of the Skulls, the place of execution. He also bought ropes, but when he saw these, Longinus sent him back for the immissa cross and spikes and a sledge.

"He is not to be roped," said Longinus. "He is to be nailed, that he may die quicker."

But this time news that a man was to be crucified had spread through the city. When then the rabbi was at last led out of the fortress, a crowd had collected to follow him and see who he was. Some said it was the rabbi of Nazareth who was to be crucified, but others said that it was only one who had posed as the rabbi of Nazareth, and so was deserving of death. Few indeed could recognize the bloodied wretch who staggered under the weight of the heavy immissa down the steps of the Antonia which led to the street, and along the street up the hill to the city gate beyond which lay the Hill of the Skulls.

When the crowd first saw him they were filled with pity. The rabbi had gone but a few paces before the upright of the cumbersome immissa, which he had on his back, caught on a stone and he was thrown down by it. Immediately one of the soldiers who was carrying a scourge for this purpose fell on him, beating him unmercifully with the scourge. Then there was a curious reaction among the crowd which Longinus had witnessed before. Seeing the thongs descend on the quivering body of the rabbi, pity turned to revulsion, and revulsion to hatred—not hatred against the soldier who was using the scourge but hatred against the victim trying miserably to rise and suffering so disgustingly before them.

The crowd urged the soldier to lay on harder, and called the rabbi foul names, and some flung the dung of camels and asses at him. Balba, a veteran of crucifixions, realized that the rabbi could never get up between the weight of the cross he carried and the blows of the soldier. So he pushed the soldier aside and lifted the cross up himself, and the rabbi got to his feet.

Longinus was mounted, using his horse to clear a way through the mob. He had become again a soldier of Rome, hardening his heart so that he could do his duty, but he could hardly look at the rabbi and control his anger against the crowd. Part of his duty demanded that nobody interfere with the prisoner whose punishment was to be no more and no less than that laid down by the order of execution. So, when he saw a man strike the rabbi, who had now got to his feet, he rode down on him and hit him on the side of the head with the flat of his sword.

"Don't touch the prisoner of Rome," he commanded. "You have no license to strike him. Balba, clear the mob back." Balba, grinning, reversed the heavy pilum, or spear, he carried and, using the thick shaft as a quarter-staff, beat the people off until there was room for the rabbi to proceed. But they had scarcely cleared the gate in the city walls before the rabbi fell down again, and this time one of the women in the crowd ran to him and, ignoring the scourge of the soldier, wiped his face with a napkin for it was bathed in blood.

Now it was forbidden under the sentence of execution for anyone to show any sympathy for a condemned man, and Longinus pressed his horse over to the woman and told her to move away. "You may not touch him," he said to the woman. "What is your name?"

"Veronica. I was a leper and he cured me. I cannot watch him suffer and not help though you kill me."

"Move away," said the centurion, his face hard. There were other women around and he said to them, "Let none of you come near him." Again the rabbi tried to get to his feet, and he did so, and went a few steps, only to fall once more. Again the scourge was produced, but at this point Longinus dismounted and stretched an arm over the rabbi to prevent the thongs falling.

The rabbi had rolled over on his back, the cross lying part way over him. His breath was feeble and he was losing so much blood that plainly he was no longer up to the task of carrying it.

They had at this time reached a point outside the walls near one of the main roads which entered Jerusalem by the gate. Several were passing on the road, and one of them came over to see what the confusion was about. This man pushed his way through the mob, and Longinus saw at a glance from the clothing he was wearing that he was not a Jew but a Gentile.

"You," he said. "Pick up that cross and carry it for this man."

"Me?" cried the stranger. "I have nothing to do with these people. I am a peaceful man and don't want to interfere."

"What is your name?" asked Longinus.

"Simon. I am from Cyrene. I am already delayed on my journey. I was to have been in the city before the start of the Jewish feast."

"Then a little more delay won't hurt you," said the centurion. "Pick up the cross and carry it." So the man bent and picked the cross off the rabbi and put it on his own shoulders. He moved fast with it up the Hill of the Skulls, and when he had got it there he threw it on the ground and ran back to the road.

Caiphas and the others of the Pharisees had not followed the rabbi through the streets, not wanting to be contaminated by the mob. They were waiting apart outside the city walls, and they grumbled at the centurion's giving the cross to another man and complained to him that it was contrary to the sentence, which insisted that each man condemned to execution must carry the instrument of his own death himself. They would, they said, report him to Pilate for showing mercy to the rabbi.

"Why then," said Longinus, "if I have done wrong, fetch the cross yourself back here, and I will then have the rabbi carry it."

To this Caiphas made no reply, and the rabbi was dragged the rest of the way up the hill by a rope which was tied around his waist.

CHAPTER TWENTY-NINE

The rabbi and his executioners reached the summit of the Hill of the Skulls a little before midday. There were already two felons on crosses on the hill, and these brigands were affixed to the tau cross with ropes so that they would be a long time dying. One went into a paroxysm of muscle spasms when they arrived and shrieked for water and then, in the middle of a shriek, became unconscious.

He was, like his fellow, suffocating. The weight of his body on his bound arms produced a spasm which paralyzed the muscles of his chest, so that he was unable to expel the air in his lungs. To obtain relief, he was obliged to thrust upward with his feet, taking his weight on his bound ankles. But he could hold this position for only a breath or two when he was obliged to bear the weight on his arms again, experiencing another muscle spasm and inability to breathe. Death on the cross then was death resulting from self-inflicted suffocation to be achieved only by self-torture, and the two bound men would remain alive, enduring the tortures of muscle spasm, suffocation, and relief, until their legs failed them and they would suffocate.

The same fate, a little hastened, now awaited the rabbi. He would die faster from loss of blood, but the muscle spasms resulting from the weight on his arms would still trap the air in his chest and to relieve this he would have to push up with his feet, putting his whole weight on the spikes driven through them. These would cut farther and farther up the feet, under his weight, until stopped by the ankle joint, when the rabbi would have a firm purchase to thrust against when he wanted a breath. But the constant loss of blood would weaken him and if he did not bleed to death first, he would soon be too weak to thrust upward with his legs and so suffocate.

The rabbi was first stripped of his clothing, which came off matted with blood from the scourging. His whole body was quivering from shock and torture, but, without a murmur, he lay down himself on the cross, and Longinus took the bag of spikes which he had been carrying on the saddle of his horse and threw them to Balba and the other three soldiers, together with a small sledge hammer. So heavy a hammer was not needed to pierce the flesh but to drive the spike into the tough cypress wood of which the cross was made. Balba picked up one of the spikes and, putting a knee on the arm of the rabbi to hold it steady, threw the hammer to another soldier.

"You drive," he said. "My eyes aren't good."

"Afraid you might hit his arm and hurt him?" asked the soldier, grinning.

"Shut up," said Balba. He positioned the spike on the rabbi's wrist, for it would tear out if driven through the palm of the hand, and said, "All right. Drive it."

One blow was sufficient to put the spike clear through the wrist, and three more through the wood of the cross. It surprised Balba that when the spike was driven, the rabbi's fist did not clench in a spasm nor his arm jerk. He turned to look at him to see if he had fainted but found him still conscious.

Up to this point Balba had had no feelings about the rabbi, but now he felt a little sorry for him. An old hand at executions, he had made some personal provision out of his experience for this one. This consisted of filling his water bottle, which was a large sponge contained in a cloth, with pure wine instead of vinegar and water, which was the regulation drink. This served to get him a little drunk and so dull his senses to the shriekings of those crucified. But now he reached for his wine bottle, took out the sponge and pressed it to the rabbi's mouth.

"Here," he said. "Drink this. It's pure wine. I brought it for myself but you take all you want. You won't feel the pain so much." But the rabbi moved his head away, and to Balba's surprise there were tears in his eyes.

Immediately Balba felt so piercing a pain in his own eyes that he dropped the sponge and clapped his hands over them. The pain remained for several seconds and then subsided as quickly as it had come, and he removed his hands, trembling, expecting that he would now be blind. Then he cried out, "I can see. I can see. The rabbi has cured me." But the crowd laughed, believing that Balba was mocking the reputed powers of the rabbi.

"It is true," cried Balba to the centurion. "The rabbi has restored my sight."

"Get on with your job," said Longinus, his face hard.

"Me?" cried Balba. "Not I. Not if I am crucified myself."

"Do you think yourself greater than I?" asked the centurion. "You are a soldier of Rome and your orders are to kill him."

"Then a curse on Rome," said Balba. But he was afraid when he said that and returned to the cross though he would take up neither the nails nor the hammer and the other three had to finish the nailing.

When all the spikes had been driven it was the centurion's job to insure that the work was properly done, and he did this and then himself affixed the superscription over the head of the cross. Then, using tackles and a ring which was affixed to a boulder on the summit of the hill for this purpose, the crucifix was hauled erect so that its foot was thrust into a hole dug for this purpose. It was fastened erect by driving small boulders and wedges around the foot in the hole, and all that remained now was for the centurion to stand guard with his men to see that none touched the rabbi, either to rescue him or bring about his death by any method other than crucifixion.

There were indeed none to rescue him. Of his followers only the man John had come with him to the crucifixion and he stood with the women near the cross, comforting an older one among them who was identified as the mother of the rabbi.

Now the Pharisees and scribes, ignoring the sobs of the women, and indeed incited by them, mocked at the rabbi, hissing at him and wagging their heads in that gesture of mockery that was peculiar to them and reminded the centurion of geese.

"Save yourself now, rabbi, son of God," said one. "Come on down from the cross, and we will worship you."

"He can save others, but he can't save himself," cried another. "Behold the Messiah of Israel surrounded by his heavenly army—two thieves."

"Since you are to die will you not now admit that all your miracles were only tricks?" cried Caiphas. "Come. On the eve of death, speak the truth for once in your life."

And so they continued, until they had run out of jibes and could think of nothing more to say, but fell to joking among themselves about the many miracles the rabbi had claimed to perform, only to end a crucified felon.

This seemed to them a huge jest, and every time the rabbi, seized by a muscle spasm, thrust upward with his feet to gasp for breath, they mocked his agony and his helplessness. One wit asked whether they ought not to send for Lazarus, who certainly owed him a favor and might save him, but another parried that the rabbi must die first, when perhaps Lazarus would even the score by raising him from the dead.

One hour went by and then another. And every minute of each hour the rabbi had to push against the spikes which pierced his feet, writhing upward to release his breath which came out each time with a groan of agony. A couple of times Balba put his sponge on the end of his spear and reached it up to the mouth of the rabbi so that he could drink to ease his sufferings, but each time it was refused.

Although none were supposed to come near the cross, Longinus allowed the rabbi's mother and the only disciple who had remained faithful to him, John of Zebedee, to approach it. John stood close to the mother of the rabbi, holding her head on his breast, to comfort her. He himself never took his face off the rabbi's, nor ceased from weeping; and the rabbi, seeing his mother and his disciple standing there, said to them, "Mother, behold your son. Son, behold your mother." These were the ancient words of the dying, commending someone to another's care, and so sacred a charge would be honored while either lived.

Longinus himself could scarcely bare to look at the rabbi. He felt himself now an accursed man who had rewarded good with evil. When he looked at the bloodied face of the rabbi, he saw in it the sum total of his life's work—violence, punishment and death inflicted on those incapable of defending themselves. There was no help for this. It was the condition of life among men, and yet he hated it.

At length, the interval between muscle spasms became longer and longer and the rabbi began lapsing into unconsciousness for brief periods from loss of blood. During one of these periods the centurion believed him dead and took hope that the agony of the rabbi was now over. But then the rabbi stirred and started weakly to heave himself up again and cried out, "My God, my God, why have you forsaken me!"

This was more than the centurion could stand. He snatched the pilum from Balba. He put the head of the spear under the rabbi's chest and, placing both hands on the shaft, heaved upward hard, driving the spearhead into the heart so that part of the shaft itself was buried in his body. Then he pulled out the spear, but all that followed it from the terrible wound he had made was a little blood and water and he knew that the rabbi was already dead and his gift of death, which was all he had to give, had come too late.

At that, he wept.

CHAPTER THIRTY

When the rabbi was dead a soldier came out of the city with further orders for Longinus from Pilate. "Their legs are to be broken," he said. "The Jews don't want anyone on the crosses during their Sabbath tomorrow."

"See to it then," said the centurion. "But do not touch the rabbi. He is dead already. He is not to be mutilated further."

He then mounted his horse and turned to ride down to the city. He rode hard so that he would not hear the hammers smash into the legs of the two thieves as the shinbones were broken so they could not heave themselves upward any more.

He felt more weary than he had ever felt in his life. Nothing he had seen done or had been obliged to do himself in all his service had taken as heavy a toll of him as the crucifixion of the rabbi. He had once had a fondness for the Jews but he now hated them with a fierce hate because they had killed the rabbi of Nazareth, and they had made him do the killing. They had used him as the tool of their murder, for that is what it seemed to him to be.

Of all the people he had known, the Jews now seemed to him the most despicable, and he thought with savage contempt of the disciples who had followed the rabbi, led by the fisherman Peter, who had all fled in fear as soon as the rabbi was arrested. Indeed of the lepers and blind and deaf and paralyzed he had cured, only one, the woman Veronica, had been with him at the end. And in this black mood he rode through the gates of the city to report to Pilate that the rabbi was dead.

As he galloped his horse over the cobbles past the walls of the Antonia, he caught a glimpse of a figure with its back toward him leaning on the wall. He recognized the man immediately and reined his horse in, dismounted and crossed to him.

He seized the man by the shoulder and whirled him around and shouted, "Coward of a Jew! Where were you, Peter of Capernaum, when they killed your rabbi?" Then he struck Peter with the back of his hand, and struck him again and again until the blood spurted from his nose and his lips. At last he stopped for the look on the man's face, bloodied from the blows, was precisely that on the face of the rabbi when he was crucified. The man's eyelids were red from tears and lack of sleep and his eyes dark with utter loneliness and abandonment.

"Strike again, Centurion," Peter said. "Strike again. I beg you."

But Longinus could not strike another blow, but only stared at the man for, though alive, he looked dead. He was shivering as if with the ague, and the centurion turned to his horse and took off it the cloak of the rabbi which his soldiers had given to him. He put it around Peter's shoulders and said, "You have need of it." Then he remounted his horse and rode off to see Pilate.

Pilate did not receive him immediately, and when he was summoned to the procurator's presence he found there Caiphas and the Roman Jew Saul and another man whom he did not know.

"What brings you here?" said Pilate.

"I came to report that the rabbi is dead, and ask for your further orders," said the centurion.

"So soon?" said Pilate. "You are sure?"

"Quite sure," said Longinus. "I drove the pilum into his heart myself."

"My congratulations," said Pilate. "You have done your duty well. That other matter is forgotten. It will never again be remembered."

"If he is dead," said the man whom Longinus did not know, "may his body be turned over to me for burial? There is just time before the start of the Sabbath for him to be quickly anointed and entombed. An hour perhaps."

"You have a place for him?" asked Pilate.

"Yes. My own tomb."

"Why such concern over a felon?" asked Pilate cautiously. "Do you now want to honor and make a hero of the man who called himself the king of the Jews? I warn you that I will not stand for anything of that sort."

"Excellency," said the man, "it is not as the king of the Jews that I would bury him, but as a just and holy man who was put to death by a portion of the Sanhedrin, led by Caiphas here, and without the knowledge of others who would have voted against it."

"He blasphemed," said Caiphas. "I have witnesses."

The other man said nothing.

"You have any objection to the body being surrendered to Joseph of Arimathea?" asked Pilate of Caiphas.

"I have only this objection," said Caiphas. "This rabbi

said that he would die and on the third day after his death he would rise from the dead. I would like a guard put on the tomb to frustrate any plot of his followers to steal the body and then proclaim that he has risen from the dead as he prophesied. For if such a thing happens, matters will be far worse than if he were never crucified."

"On the third day?" said Pilate. "Not the first day or the second day?"

"No. The third day."

"Curious," said Pilate. "There is some mystical significance attached to the number three. My wife Procula would be interested in it. Well, I will set such a guard. The centurion here is tired, so I will put others to guard on the first and the second day. But for you, Centurion, a gift to set your heart at rest concerning the rabbi of Nazareth."

"What gift?" asked Longinus.

"You shall guard the tomb on the third day," said Pilate. "And that, I think, finishes the matter."